BREATHING
UNDERWATER

Also by Dr. Joe MacInnis

Underwater Images

Underwater Man

The Land That Devours Ships

Titanic in a New Light

Saving the Oceans

Fitzgerald's Storm

Surviving Terrorism:
How to Protect Your Health, Wealth and Safety

BREATHING
UNDERWATER

THE QUEST TO LIVE IN THE SEA

DR. JOE MacINNIS

VIKING
CANADA

VIKING CANADA

Published by the Penguin Group

Penguin Group (Canada), 10 Alcorn Avenue, Toronto, Ontario, Canada M4V 3B2
(a division of Pearson Penguin Canada Inc.)

Penguin Group (USA) Inc., 375 Hudson Street, New York, New York 10014, U.S.A.
Penguin Books Ltd, 80 Strand, London WC2R 0RL, England
Penguin Ireland, 25 St Stephen's Green, Dublin 2, Ireland (a division of Penguin Books Ltd)
Penguin Group (Australia), 250 Camberwell Road, Camberwell, Victoria 3124, Australia
(a division of Pearson Australia Group Pty Ltd)
Penguin Books India Pvt Ltd, 11 Community Centre, Panchsheel Park, New Delhi – 110 017,
India
Penguin Group (NZ), Cnr Airborne and Rosedale Roads, Albany, Auckland, New Zealand
(a division of Pearson New Zealand Ltd)
Penguin Books (South Africa) (Pty) Ltd, 24 Sturdee Avenue, Rosebank, Johannesburg 2196,
South Africa

Penguin Books Ltd, Registered Offices: 80 Strand, London WC2R 0RL, England

First published 2004

1 2 3 4 5 6 7 8 9 10 (FR)

Excerpt from *The Deepest Days* by Robert Stenuit,
published by Coward-McCann, 1966, used with permission.

Excerpt from *Sea Dwellers* by Robert A. Barth,
published by Doyle Publishing Co., Houston, Texas, 2000, used with permission.

Manufactured in Canada.

LIBRARY AND ARCHIVES CANADA CATALOGUING IN PUBLICATION

MacInnis, Joe, 1937–
Breathing underwater : the quest to live in the sea / Joe MacInnis.

Includes bibliographical references and index.
ISBN 0-670-04397-4

1. MacInnis, Joe, 1937–. 2. Underwater exploration. I. Title.

VM981.M29 2004 551.46'092 C2004-903486-3

Visit the Penguin Group (Canada) website at **www.penguin.ca**

INTRODUCTION

IF YOU SPEND YOUR LIFE working under the ocean, there are certain days that fall deep into memory. One of these days was June 18, 1973, when four men in a small research sub made what should have been a routine dive in the Florida Keys. Reaching the bottom at 360 feet, they attempted to recover a scientific sample, came too close to the wreckage of a U.S. Navy destroyer and became entangled in a wire hanging off its stern. Teams of salvage divers from the U.S. Naval Station in Key West tried to rescue them, but were held back by strong currents. After 16 hours, the cold and carbon dioxide in the sub's diving compartment rose to lethal levels. The two men inside lost consciousness and, in a matter of minutes, were dead. Hours later, the sub was brought to the surface, and the two men in the forward compartment were saved.

I remember standing on the wide concrete jetty at the naval station as *Sea Diver,* the sub's mother ship, came into port. There were about 20 of us watching the all-white research ship turn and come toward us. No one spoke. A soft breeze carried the smell of seaweed and brine.

The evening before, Edwin Link had called me at my Toronto office. Link was the acclaimed inventor and undersea pioneer who owned *Sea Diver*. "There's been an accident," he said in a voice that was barely audible. "Can you come down?" He told me that one of the men trapped inside the sub was his son, Clay. Never had I heard such anguish in a man's voice.

As *Sea Diver* slowed and came alongside the jetty, lines were tossed from her bow and stern to men on the jetty who tied them to a pair of steel-gray bollards. Slowly, the gap of dark water between the ship and the concrete narrowed.

⁘

Ten years earlier, as a young medical doctor, I had come to this same jetty to join Ed Link and his team of undersea explorers. I was unsure of myself and knew little about the ocean, but Link somehow understood my passion for undersea medicine and hired me to help him look after the health and safety of his divers. In the years that followed, he introduced me to a gleaming universe of diving bells, decompression chambers, sailors, scientists and undersea stations. The man who gave me my first job had an unwavering determination and an overriding sense of responsibility—to his crew, his program and his country. Building on the success of his undersea research, he founded Ocean Systems Inc., the world's largest commercial diving and undersea engineering company. During the years I was its medical director, we worked on dozens of first-ever projects—deepwater oil drilling in the North Sea, the salvage of military aircraft in the Atlantic and the celebrated recovery of the H-bomb in the Mediterranean off the coast of Spain. It was the decade when humans learned how to live in outer space and dwell in the depths of the ocean. For those of us fortunate enough to participate, it was the golden age of diving and diving research.

Three men defined this vibrant chapter of undersea exploration: Jacques Cousteau, George Bond and Ed Link. Cousteau was the charismatic Frenchman who co-invented the aqualung in 1943 and, for the next three decades, invited the world to join him in his televised undersea adventures. George Bond was the U.S. Navy physician whose pioneering research confirmed that high-pressure atmospheres were safe for humans. And Ed Link was the shy American who invented undersea stations and diver lockout submarines to give us prolonged access to the ocean's depths. As part of his long-range vision, Link organized expeditions to the Bahamas and the Florida Keys, where we tested his devices in some of the longest and deepest dives ever made. Like Bond and

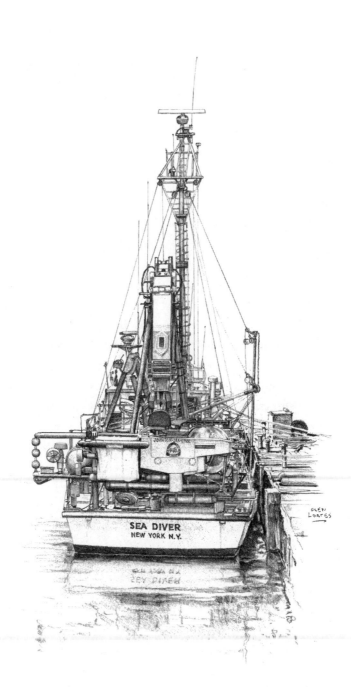

Edwin Link's RV *Sea Diver* alongside the pier in Key West
with the *Johnson-Sea-Link* research sub on her stern. *(Courtesy of Glen Loates)*

Cousteau, he never asked those who worked for him to do anything he wouldn't do himself. His courage, integrity and determination made him a man I hugely admired, even loved.

·:·:·

The mini-sub was lying in its deck-mounted cradle on *Sea Diver*'s stern. Its two-person diving chamber was partially covered with white, sun-bleached canvas. As we waited for the lifeless bodies of Clay Link and Al Stover to be decompressed, there was nothing I could do but try to comfort Ed and his wife, Marion. I didn't feel up to the task and didn't trust myself to speak. I kept thinking about how much Ed had contributed to the exploration of the inner sea. He invented strange-looking machines that allowed humans to live safely for long periods beneath the surface. He and his friend Seward Johnson Sr. established the Harbor Branch Oceanographic Institute, a renowned center for scientific diving and marine research. By example, and through the Link Foundation Fellowship program, Link had inspired many young people to commit to working inside the ocean.

That night, I decided to write a book that would celebrate the spirit and achievements of Ed Link and his fellow undersea pioneers. It would focus on the years between 1963 and 1973, years that included the horror of the Kennedy and King assassinations, the violence of the war in Vietnam and the first footprints on the moon. It would be an account of the quest to conquer the continental shelves—a submerged area the size of Africa that surrounds the continents—by learning how to live and work at the bottom of the sea. The book would describe the machines we used, the men who used them and what it was like to live in artificial, high-pressure environments.

It has taken me 30 years to figure out how to tell the story. I needed the time to reflect on the meaning of those early days and how they influenced the rest of my career. I needed to think about how good people who are generous with their time and talent could permanently shape a young man's life.

The ocean and men like Ed Link have taught me everything I know about courage, commitment and compassion. I carried something away from those years that bound me to the sea, its people and their purpose for the rest of my life. It is a memory that has guided me and kept me safe.

This book is not a chronological history. Each chapter is constructed around dramatic events and fascinating characters telling their stories through reminiscence. I have made every effort to ensure that the narrative is true to the men and their time. While not verbatim, the dialogue reflects the essence of what was said.

This book is about technology and its risks, but it is also about a small group of men who changed forever our relationship to the sea. It begins on a cold spring day in the North Atlantic.

ONE

APRIL 1963. She is war's ultimate weapon. From her smooth, round bow to her slowly rotating propeller, her massive cylindrical body spans a distance of almost 300 feet. Below the steel curves of her conning tower, which houses her periscopes and antennae, she is as high as a three-story building. She is completely black. At a depth of about 50 fathoms, she is invisible.

She is the USS *Thresher,* the lead ship of America's most advanced class of nuclear-powered attack submarine. Inside her huge pressure hull are 16 officers, 96 sailors and 17 civilians from the Portsmouth Naval Shipyard. Her commanding officer is John "Wes" Harvey, a graduate of the United States Naval Academy. *Thresher* has just spent nine months being overhauled in the shipyard, and Lieutenant Commander Harvey is beginning the second day of her sea trials.

Thresher is a lethal machine of the Cold War, one of thousands that include strategic bombers and land-based missiles built by the United States and the Soviet Union. She is part of a nuclear threat that says terrible things about forces beyond our control, about a part of our history when men are thinking seriously about killing millions of people with a weapon that creates the heat of the sun.

Yesterday, *Thresher* sailed out of the shipyard where she was launched three years earlier. On the ocean east of Boston, *Skylark,* a 205-foot-long submarine rescue vessel, joined her. Lashed onto *Skylark*'s fantail is a McCann chamber, a diving bell that can be winched down on a steel cable to rescue the survivors of a stricken submarine.

In April 1963, the American nuclear Navy consists of 30 submarines in service and another 40 in various stages of construction. They are designed to defeat the menace of an even greater number of Russian nuclear attack and ballistic missile subs operating in the Atlantic and Pacific. Behind these facts is a larger truth. During the early years of the Cold War, both Navies developed a new kind of submarine—fast, deep-diving and completely independent of the surface. Until nuclear power came along, military submarines were limited to the upper few hundred feet of the ocean. Now they range to depths five times as deep, pushing their long black hulls into an unknown universe.

The cold, dark waters of the world's oceans and its adjoining basins are the oldest and largest physical feature on the surface of the planet. More than three billion years old, they cover some 140 million square miles or 71 percent of the earth's surface with an average depth of two and a half miles of water. Within their enormous volume of 350 million cubic miles are crushing pressures, piercing cold and perpetual darkness.

In spite of the vast weight of the ocean above them and the unseen fathoms below them, the men inside *Thresher* feel secure. They are surrounded by well-lit engineering spaces and softly humming mechanical systems that give them a sense of order and command. They carry out their tasks—steering, navigation, engineering and communications—with scripted diligence. They are young and come from farms, small towns and big-city tenements across the United States. They are loyal to each other and their ship, and there is a rough assurance in the way they work and in the way they talk to each other in nonchalant, teasing voices. Most of them have made this kind of voyage many times before.

Yesterday, *Thresher* conducted a series of shallow tests over the continental shelf, the submerged shoulder of North America that begins at the shoreline and descends to a depth of 600 feet. Worldwide, these broad, shallow regions adjacent to the continents lie under almost 8 percent of the total ocean and form the boundary of the deep ocean basins. While underwater, *Thresher* communicated at regular intervals to *Skylark* through her UQC, or underwater telephone system. Because of differences in water density and temperature, the transmission between the two vessels was frequently distorted.

The nuclear attack submarine USS *Thresher* running under power on the surface of the Atlantic Ocean. (*Courtesy of Glen Loates*)

Last night, her shallow tests completed, *Thresher* headed east, out over the edge of the continental shelf. This morning, the water below her keel is more than 8,000 feet deep.

As always, the unknown energies flowing through the ocean in which the huge sub is suspended include up-wellings and down-wellings and sliding layers of currents and near-freezing temperatures. These energies haunt *Thresher*'s every move. Some of the older men inside her pressure hull regard them with distrust. They know they are inside a machine made up of several million parts and pieces, and each one has been designed, fabricated, tested and installed by someone who is now on land. Any fear is hidden behind small gestures, old habits and practiced rituals.

At 6:35 A.M., following a radio check with *Skylark*, *Thresher*'s crew begin the procedures that will take her to her maximum operating depth. Directly below her conning tower is a small room called the command and control center. Inside, a dozen men, including her skipper, are standing or sitting in front of display consoles, instrument panels, chart stands and plotting tables. Just above their heads are gray pipes, black wires and red phone boxes.

At 8:10 A.M., *Skylark* receives the following message on her underwater acoustic telephone:

"We are now at 400 feet."

At 400 feet, the pressure on *Thresher*'s hull is almost 200 pounds per square inch. In a few minutes, when she reaches 1,000 feet, the pressure will increase to 445 pounds per square inch.

Thresher's massive hull is a series of steel rings and two end domes welded together into a single unit. It is designed to operate safely down to depths of 1,000 feet. Beyond 1,500 feet—called the "crush depth"—it will rupture.

Despite the hull's ability to withstand immense pressures, it is penetrated by dozens of pipes, periscopes, access hatches and torpedo tubes, as well as the propeller shaft. One of the reasons for this dive is to inspect the integrity of every valve, pipe and seal throughout the ship.

At 9:10 A.M., *Thresher* descends through 900 feet. Her circular frames groan under the pressure, her bulkheads creak. Throughout the length of the submarine, from the torpedo room to the wardroom, from the reactor compartment to the main engine room, groups of men study instruments and dials. The officers are experts in physics, electrical engineering, heat transfer, reactor theory and radiological control. The members of the crew are among the most carefully selected and best trained in the Navy. The men with the most responsibility are thinking fast and working quickly. Some off-duty men are sleeping.

Without warning, there is a hard, sharp sound in a machinery space behind the reactor. A narrow pipe filled with seawater bursts open.

As word of the emergency spreads through the three-story vessel, men rush to repair the damage, but the cold water roaring out of the pipe fills the room with a freezing fog, tearing out wires, flooding control panels and short-circuiting electrical switches. Circuit breakers trip. Panels go dead. Officers call out hoarse commands. Sailors respond with subdued voices and rapid movements. Minutes later, *Thresher's* nuclear reactor shuts down and her turbines lose steam. The 4,000-ton submarine slows to a stop, stalls and begins to slide backward toward the center of the earth.

At 9:13 A.M., Lieutenant Commander Harvey reaches for the phone and calls *Skylark*.

"Experiencing minor difficulty. Have positive up-angle. Attempting to blow."

These are words the men on board *Skylark* have never heard before. They lean in toward their radio trying to understand their meaning. They hear the sound of air moving under high pressure, as if *Thresher's* men are trying to bring her to the surface by forcing water out of her ballast tanks. Three minutes later they hear a distorted voice saying:

"Exceeding test depth."

Inside *Thresher,* streams of visual and auditory information are overwhelming the men in the command center. Everything tells them that the steel protecting them from the ocean is about to give way. Some men are breathing so fast they can't handle the rush of air going in and out of their lungs.

Inside the saline darkness, *Thresher* descends through gathering forces. Somewhere below her crush depth, driven by the weight of half a mile of water, the ocean slams through a section of her hull, tearing away bulkheads, filling every space with super-heated air at a pressure of more than 700 pounds per square inch. Lights go out. Motors stop running. Throughout the sub, things break and smash together. Diesel fuel and hydraulic fluid ignite. Some men are blown against instrument panels and impaled on pipes. Arms and legs are sheared off. Men are torn open and burned, their bodies reduced to smoke. The suffering is brief; everyone dies within seconds.

The thunderous implosion breaks *Thresher* into three large pieces.

After falling through several thousand feet of water, *Thresher*'s remains hit the sea floor at more than 70 miles an hour, digging deep impact craters. Her nuclear reactor buries itself under several yards of sediment. For hours afterward, the contents of her interior, including torn sheets of insulation, pieces of matting, charts and clothing, descend slowly through the water. According to its weight and shape, each object is drawn down-current into a long, curving debris trail. Toward the end of the day, lighter materials, including a blizzard of torn envelopes, candy wrappers, crushed cigarette packs, pages of half-written letters, dollar bills and faded photographs, are still leafing onto the sediments. Far above on the surface, all is distance, gray water and sky.

Thresher has fallen to the depths of Earth's second-largest ocean. The Atlantic covers nearly 32 million square miles and runs from the Arctic to the Antarctic. The South Atlantic is a barren realm of water with only a few islands, including the Falklands and Ascension, breaking its monotonous surge and sweep. The North Atlantic is an ocean of immense variety; it includes the Mediterranean Sea on its eastern flank and the Caribbean, the Gulf of Mexico and the Gulf of St. Lawrence on its western. *Thresher* has disappeared into the blackness and landed on a poorly charted, little-known sea floor.

Within hours of her loss, other U.S. Navy vessels steam out to join *Skylark* at *Thresher*'s last known position. The sailors on board are searching for traces in the water with eyes and minds blunted by the fact that the pride of the fleet has been swallowed by the sea, taking 129 good men with her, men like themselves with brush-cuts and cowlicks, men who were friendly and capable and quick.

The two dozen sailors on *Skylark* are still trying to make sense of the words "exceeding test depth," spoken in a voice with its color and shading drained out. Then there was the hard thump followed by the loud implosion, a sound so powerful it reverberated through the depths of the ocean and was picked up hundreds of miles away by the hydrophones of the Navy's underwater surveillance system.

The officers commanding the gathering of ships converse in subdued voices. How did this happen? Is there a flaw in *Thresher*'s design? Are her sister subs carrying the same flaw? Some officers are secretly relieved to be commanding ships that float on the surface. It is their unspoken belief that steering a 4,000-ton vessel into the depths is a game of chance played with every dive.

⋯⋄⋯

Everyone knows that rescue is not an option. What's left of *Thresher* lies deeper than 8,000 feet. The Navy's primary rescue device, the McCann chamber, works only to 850 feet.

As the days pass, the Navy's objective turns to finding the lost sub and determining the cause of the accident. Because warships are not equipped to search the bottom of the sea, the Navy asks the scientific community for help. Among the first to respond are the deepwater scientists at Woods Hole Oceanographic Institute on nearby Cape Cod.

As soon as the deepwater search begins, it becomes apparent that trying to locate an object lying under a mile and a half of ocean—even something as large as a nuclear submarine—is almost impossible. The search ships lack precision navigation systems and their tracks across the surface may be in error by as much as 300 yards. This means that a 100-yard-long object on the bottom could easily be missed. And when deep-sea cameras are lowered into the abyss, mid-water currents push them in unknown directions.

After two weeks, the Navy's plotting charts show about a hundred possible "contacts." Unfortunately, so little is known about the sea floor in this part of the North Atlantic that it is impossible to distinguish between normal geological features and objects of human construction. As the weeks pass, the *Thresher* disaster becomes an assault on the U.S. Navy's confidence.

The Navy persists, and in time a new deep-sea camera from MIT provides hundreds of photos of the wreck, including torn sheets of steel and twisted pipes. Taken together, they provide a rough map of *Thresher's* main pieces and the debris field that surrounds them.

Back in Washington, the Navy is being challenged: What about the nuclear reactor? Will it explode or contaminate the surrounding waters? The reactor contains more than 20 tons of fuel rods holding enriched uranium and deadly by-products such as plutonium. People want to know if the radioactivity will affect the health of the ocean.

In June, the *Trieste* is brought to the site. The U.S. Navy's only vehicle capable of surviving at *Thresher's* depth, the *Trieste* is a big and ungainly bathyscaphe and looks like a throwback to a lost mechanical age. Her main feature is a thin steel tank 60 feet long and 12 feet wide, and filled with 34,000 gallons of lighter-than-water gasoline. Suspended beneath it is a seven-foot steel pressure sphere that holds her three-man crew in the kneeling position. Jammed into her awkward architecture are 16 tons of steel pellets that are released when the pilot wants to surface. In simple terms, *Trieste* is an up-and-down elevator; horizontally, she is about as maneuverable as a slug on a saltlick.

On *Trieste's* fourth dive to 8,400 feet, her crew spot a yellow plastic shoe cover, the kind used by sailors inside the reactor compartment, lying on top of the tan-colored sediment. Printed on its sole is SSN-593, *Thresher's* ship numbers. Several days later, *Trieste's* crew take pictures of part of the debris field containing shredded electrical cables, twisted battery plates and large pieces of superstructure. As the weeks go by, they use mechanical manipulators mounted on *Trieste* to recover debris that might point to the cause of the accident.

At the court of inquiry convened at the Portsmouth Naval Shipyard, Admiral Hyman Rickover is asked about the reactor. He states that it is "physically impossible for the reactor to explode like a bomb ... the core of the reactor is well protected from seawater corrosion."

Two weeks after the disaster, the Secretary of the Navy organizes the first meeting of the Deep Submergence Systems Review Group, 60 experts in oceanography, underwater engineering and submarine operations. They are asked to study the accident and assess the U.S. Navy's capabilities in the deep ocean environment. In the months that follow, these distinguished admirals, scientists and engineers devote themselves to their task with determination and discipline. Behind every thought and every decision is the image of a black-hulled submarine, as long as a football field, her living quarters, wardroom and control center slowly falling through the ocean until there is a sound so violent that it bursts every eardrum, collapses every lung and stops every heart almost simultaneously. One hundred and twenty-nine men are now dead, the remains of their bodies diffusing slowly into the currents and nearby sediments.

The head of the group's civilian sector is a wealthy inventor-businessman in his late fifties. Edwin A. Link began his career during the first third of the twentieth century, when aviation was changing from conquest of the air to an essential mail service. In those days, the rules of safe flying were still being made up in the cockpit. In a fog or thunderstorm, a pilot's instruments couldn't be trusted, so he flew "by the seat of his pants." By 1923, this undisciplined approach had killed 31 airmail pilots.

As a high school dropout who flew the same skies as Charles Lindbergh and Amelia Earhart, Ed Link worried about the fatalities. His response was to invent a device that would allow pilots to acquire their flying skills without leaving the ground. Using abilities he had mastered in his father's organ factory in Binghamton, New York, he mounted a stubby wooden cockpit and fuselage on top of a pedestal containing an organ bellows. An electrically driven vacuum pump moved the bellows in and out, causing the fuselage to pitch and roll as the pilot "flew" it. As the years passed, Link's invention, called the Link trainer, was modified and improved upon until it became a rapidly expanding commercial enterprise. During the Second World War, advanced versions saved countless lives and led to dramatic improvements in instrument flying, navigation techniques and simulators for commercial airline pilots. By 1963, the descendents of the Link trainer were helping train *Mercury* and *Gemini* astronauts and were the technical heart of a billion-dollar industry.

In the 1950s, the father of the simulation industry began focusing his engineering proficiencies on another frontier, the ocean. He started by searching for Spanish treasure ships lost in the sunlit shallows off the east coast of Florida. Working with Mendel Peterson, the Smithsonian Institution's diving curator of naval history, he recovered material from an eighteenth-century British frigate. Then, supported by the National Geographic Society and using bottom-sounding and metal-detecting devices, he conducted the first underwater archeological survey of the sunken city of Port Royal in Jamaica. He built a research ship called *Sea Diver* and sailed across the Atlantic to the Mediterranean. In the Sea of Galilee, using his own search techniques, Link discovered the remains of an ancient city.

Link's genius was in building machines that solved problems. After thinking about what he had learned from spending hundreds of hours underwater, he decided that working divers needed a device to protect them from cold, wetness and pressure. He built a combination diving bell and decompression chamber that carried two divers to the ocean floor, allowed them to exit for work and then carried them back to the surface. He called his new underwater elevator a submersible decompression chamber, or SDC.

In 1962, with support from the U.S. Navy's Sixth Fleet, Link lowered his submersible chamber into the Mediterranean off the south of France and suspended it beneath his ship at 60 feet. Then he dove down, entered the chamber and began breathing a mixture of oxygen and helium. He remained inside for the next eight hours. It was the first time that anyone had breathed this synthetic gas mixture for such a long time under the ocean.

It took Link and his associates on the Deep Submergence Systems Review Group months to absorb all the details surrounding the loss of the *Thresher.* The outcome was a report to the Navy, written in language that conveyed the authority of men well acquainted with the interior of the ocean. The report charged that nuclear submarines were routinely using depths far beyond the U.S. Navy's capabilities to rescue them. In it, they recommended that a major effort be made to improve the Navy's ability to recover personnel from sunken submarines and to salvage objects from the ocean floor. One priority, they wrote, was to develop the engineering systems and techniques to permit divers to work on the ocean floor at the 600-foot depths of the continental shelf. The report went on to urge that its recommendations be carried out as soon as possible, pointing out that if *Thresher* had sunk on the outer margins of the continental shelf, her crew would have lived on for weeks in a world unable to save them from a prolonged and agonizing death.

TWO

SEPTEMBER 1963. It is five months after the loss of *Thresher*. The inventor of the Link trainer, wearing a short-sleeved white shirt with a Deep Submergence Systems Review Group identification tag pinned on its pocket, motions me into his office. Of medium height, there is something in his manner and movement that expands his physical presence. He has a round, sun-tanned face, but his thick, horn-rimmed eyeglasses make him look like an Ivy League English professor.

"Sit down," he says, pointing to the wooden chair in front of his desk. The desk has gunmetal gray sides and is covered with technical manuals, yellow writing pads and a black rotary telephone. Behind him, an open window looks out on a row of salvage ships and minesweepers tied up to the docks and piers of the Washington Navy Yard. Beyond them the Anacostia River gleams like glass.

Link stares at me with dark green eyes. He sees a 26-year-old doctor who has just completed his junior internship at a Canadian teaching hospital. Link's eyes have the look of a man in a hurry with an uncluttered view of where he is going.

"Exactly what is it you want?" he asks. I can feel him scrutinizing my wrinkled blazer. I struggle to find the right words.

Since arriving at the Washington Navy Yard, with its red brick buildings steeped in naval history, my heart has been wedged in my shoes. From what I have read in *National Geographic* magazine, I know that the U.S. Navy assigned doctors to Link's previous projects. All he has to do is ask and the Navy will appoint another. My chances of joining his team are as slim as a hairline fracture.

"I'd like to work with you, sir," I offer. "As a doctor. On your next project." The sweat gathers under my arms.

"What are your qualifications?" Link glances at his watch.

I hesitate. I have been trying to arrange a face-to-face meeting with Edwin Link for two months, and when I finally reached him on the phone yesterday, he told me he could talk to me this morning but only for 15 minutes. Stretching the truth to the breaking point, I told him I was going to be in Washington on other business and asked what time I should be in his office. When I hung up I discovered it was too late to catch the last flight from Toronto so I drove all night, steering my old Pontiac around the western shore of Lake Ontario and then south and east through the Appalachians. This morning, as the sun rose out of the forest north of Gettysburg, I was so tired I didn't see the deer bounding out from the trees and across the highway. I swerved, but struck the deer broadside. The creature was killed instantly and the car was a steaming wreck. I hitchhiked into Gettysburg and rented another car. I am two hours late. My body feels as though I have been shooting up with Novocain.

"I have a degree from the University of Toronto medical school," I say slowly, "and I have just completed a year of internship at the Toronto General Hospital." I take a deep breath and press onward. "I've been scuba diving for 10 years. I'm fascinated by the challenge of trying to live under the sea."

Link looks at me. "Do you have any idea how difficult the challenge is?"

"To be honest, sir, no. But I do know that it includes serious medical questions. How well can the human body withstand the cold and pressure? What is the best breathing gas to use at different depths?"

I am in over my head. What little I know about diving medicine has been fished out of medical journals. If Link asks any hard questions, I'll go up in smoke.

He inquires if I have any experience with decompression sickness and I tell him about the night I was working in the hospital's emergency department and the police called to say there was a tunnel worker on a

The author examining John McGean, a tunnel worker on the Toronto
subway, for signs of decompression sickness. *(Courtesy of Glen Loates)*

subway construction project with severe pain in his arms and legs. I describe how I drove to the tunnel site, made the diagnosis and called the police to help me speed the man to the nearest decompression chamber at the University of Buffalo, 90 miles away.

Link is looking for assurances that I am more than the sum of my résumé. I give him some answers that are satisfactory and others that are clearly not. I can almost hear him thinking: the ocean's depths are going to impose serious stresses on the human body—can I trust this young man to help us, or would I be better off with an older Navy doctor who has been around the block once or twice?

At one point, he takes off his glasses and stares at me. "And what are your personal objectives in all this?"

I take a deep breath. "To learn as much as I can, as soon as I can. Sir."

These are the words of someone who is desperate for a sea-going job. My three-year rendezvous with hospitals has left me with an abiding dislike of being confined indoors. Too much confinement and you begin to believe that there is no such thing as fresh air and physical challenge. What I want more than anything is a life rich with meaning and purpose.

There is a long pause. I hear a group of men talking and laughing in the courtyard below the window.

"You say you are from Canada?"

I nod, certain the interview is over because I have the wrong passport.

Link swivels in his chair and looks out the window at three white-uniformed sailors walking across the yard. A beam of sunlight slants across his shoulder.

"My wife and I have a log cabin on a lake in northern Quebec," he says quietly. "We love to take a few days off in the summer, fly up there in my floatplane and go fishing. One of the most fascinating things about your country is its wilderness. It's a great place to dream about the future. I wish I could spend more time up there."

Link turns his chair back in my direction. "What was your academic standing in medical school?" he asks. The wistful tone has left his voice.

It is the one question I hoped he wouldn't ask.

"I was not a good student," I say slowly.

"Why?"

The look on his face tells me that this is a man who will not be finessed, so I answer the question directly. "Many of the professors were uninspiring and much of the work was boring. Also, I was too interested in other things. Like diving and writing."

I stop and feel myself hanging by a thread to the will of his mind, the demands of his work or something as simple as his mood of the day. He looks at his watch again. The conversation is over. "Would you like to see our research ship?" he asks. He stands up and looks out the window toward the far end of the yard and the great gleaming river.

When I stand up and straighten my legs, my chair makes a high, squeaking sound.

As we descend the stairs to the ground floor, Link says nothing. He opens the door ahead of me and we step out into the warm September sun. I look across at the low, redbrick buildings that house the Office of Naval Oceanography and the Experimental Diving Unit. The Washington Navy Yard was established in 1799, during the era of wooden-hulled ships. Fleets of ocean-going vessels sustained the first Americans who, not long after declaring their independence, created a small Navy to protect themselves. Within these walls are memories of John Paul Jones, the War of 1812 and the Civil War. Just around the corner in a three-story building, Navy divers and doctors at the Experimental Diving Unit use large compression chambers to test their most advanced diving systems and techniques.

I glance over at Ed Link's sun-weathered face. The notion of the frontier is hard-wired into the American soul. First it was the Appalachians and then it was the Great Plains. Now it is outer space and the depths of the sea.

We are surrounded by the hard-muscled work of a military waterfront with its blunt, gray ships, goods stacked on the docks, skyhook cranes and men calling to each other above the watery hum of traffic on the river. The sight of it makes me realize that I have no idea what the ocean is—nothing, that is, except what I have picked up from a few brief dives. All I know about the ocean is that it can be as treacherous as hell. When I read about the loss of *Thresher,* I could imagine the fear of those inside her. The ocean found one small flaw in a craft of meticulous construction, and destroyed it.

To fill the silence, I cautiously ask Link about his work with the Deep Submergence Systems Review Group. "We should not have lost all those men," he says, looking straight ahead. "It confirms how little we know about the depths of the ocean."

He begins talking, as if addressing a larger audience. "First, there is the immense problem of trying to locate a lost nuclear sub in deep water. Every sub should have a distress buoy that would automatically rise to the surface and send out an SOS."

Two young officers cross our path and smile at him. He gives them a shy wave. "To rescue the crew," he continues, "we need a sub small enough to fit inside a military cargo plane, a sub that can dive to 3,000 feet." He stops and looks at me, or, it seems, through me. "Much of the work we need to do under the ocean depends on being able to live underwater for long periods, swimming out from pressurized vehicles or undersea stations. Our objective is sustained access to the world's continental shelves—down to a depth of 600 feet. If successful, we'll open up an area of more than ten million square miles."

Less than a minute later, we are standing on a concrete pier next to his ship, *Sea Diver.* I hear the low murmur of water brushing against her white steel hull and inhale a thin plume of diesel exhaust. Link points to a gleaming aluminum cylinder on *Sea Diver's* deck.

"For our next dive we're going to place a small station on the seafloor at 400 feet. This chamber will carry two divers down to the station and return them to the surface. It's going to take a lot of hard work to get it done. Sometime in the next few months, we'll move the ship to Key West and begin a series of shallow practice dives."

Key West. My mind cradles the word. For an instant I see myself not as a doctor working inside the numbing bureaucracy of a big city hospital but as a young man for whom the world is yearning to open itself.

I follow Link up the gangway onto the sun-warmed deck and take a good look around. In the next berth is an all-gray submarine rescue vessel

with a McCann chamber. They appear so solid that it seems impossible
they could break into pieces and sink to the ocean floor. On the foredeck,
a chief petty officer is barking at a line of vigorous young sailors. In the
distance, a small tugboat moves down the river, heading for the wide salt
reaches of Chesapeake Bay.

For the next half an hour, Link shows me the highlights of his
100-foot ship, including its high-windowed pilot house jammed with
steering and engine controls, chart drawers, radar, depth sounders and an
automatic pilot; the white-painted engine room with its generators, water
distilling unit and gritty machine shop; the diving locker filled with
helmets and hoses; and the gleaming aluminum chamber lying in its
cradle under a heavy-duty crane. It is clear that *Sea Diver* is Edwin Link's
inside track to the future. His ship contains all the tools he needs to take
on the challenges hidden inside the ocean. It embodies the interweaving
of new technologies and hard, essential work.

We arrive at a large central room filled with bookcases, framed pictures
and a small working fireplace. It has large windows on its port and starboard
sides. On the wooden mantel are two anchor chain links embedded in clear
plastic. Engraved in each are the words: HMS *Bounty* 1789.

"Those were a gift from our friend Luis Marden at *National
Geographic*," says Link. "A few years ago, Luis found the wreck of the
Bounty off the coast of Pitcairn Island."

Link steps over to a round table and picks up a folder filled with
papers. "You say you are interested in writing?"

"Yes, sir. I've been interested in writing since high school. Some day
I'd like to write about the sea."

Link hands me the folder. "Why don't you look at this while I take
care of a few things? It's an article I'm working on for *National Geographic*."

He turns and disappears down a stairwell. I sit down in a chair with
his manuscript. At the top is written:

Tomorrow on the Deep Frontier
The Wet World—Three Quarters of the Planet—Awaits Us.
A Pioneer of the Depths Describes Our Exciting Future Undersea.

As I read through the typewritten pages, I begin to understand why Link and his fellow pioneers are so obsessed with undersea exploration.

Almost three quarters of our planet is virtually unexplored; almost three-quarters of our planet is virtually unused....

A determined program of oceanology would change our world by focusing attention on the huge resources of the sea....

The article states that more than one-third of the world's oil and gas reservoirs lie beneath the oceans and that as the shallow wells dry up, we will be forced to drill in waters now inaccessible. It also describes some of the deep-sea technologies that need to be developed to live and work underwater. I think of the warships I saw as we made our way across the yard. The Cold War with so many underlying motives and whirling possibilities includes a race to conquer and colonize the continental shelves. In the next section of text, Link makes a powerful, personal statement:

We have resolved to put human footprints on the moon, yet our efforts to understand the sea consists of a limited program ... an underwater NASA is imperative....

If three-quarters of our planet awaits us, then the great age of discovery did not end with Columbus, Magellan or Cook. It may well lie in the future.

The man who has written these words is a world-acclaimed pioneer in two frontiers, a self-made man as sturdy as a gun carriage. My heart races and my hands are trembling—"the great age of discovery ... may well lie in the future."

There is the sound of a woman's laugh and a few seconds later Marion Link appears in the stairwell. She is slightly taller than her husband and is wearing a dark blue dress. Her hair is neatly combed. She smiles and extends her hand.

"You're the young doctor from Canada."

We sit down and talk for a few minutes about my all-night drive through the Appalachians to Washington. She tells me that she and her husband live in Binghamton, New York, near the Susquehanna River, and have a wonderful view of the old, green mountains that run all the way to Georgia. As she talks, I notice her eyes are deep green and warm.

Ed Link joins us and, in the course of the conversation, modestly mentions that he applied for his first patent when he was 20 years old. I also learn what he thinks about formal education. "I left after my junior year in high school and it was an advantage. By missing a university education, I failed to learn my own limitations. It made it possible for me to do things that had never been done before."

As I stand up to say goodbye, Link says he wants me to go to Philadelphia to talk to Dr. Chris Lambertsen, the director of the Institute of Environmental Medicine at the University of Pennsylvania. Lambertsen is an international authority on diving medicine and, if I am thinking of a career in this field, he's the best man to talk to.

Outside the main cabin, I walk toward the stern and the gangway down to the pier. Link's SDC lies on its side a few feet above the water. I reach out and touch the chamber's aluminum shell. Link has designed what feels like the perfect hardness of the chamber to match the enormous forces of the ocean.

Standing on the deck, looking at the ship and its machinery, I have a moment of calm, when everything crystallizes. I have just spent time in the company of a man who informs the future by combining his ideas and action. For Ed Link, the ocean is a conjunction of thought, geography and mystery. I might never work for him, but I suddenly know with perfect clarity that I am in love with the strangeness of undiscovered worlds.

Edwin Link, inventor, entrepreneur and undersea explorer, wearing his favorite business attire—a face mask and wet suit. *(Courtesy of Glen Loates)*

THREE

IT IS A CLOUDLESS DAY in August of 1949. I am 12 years old, paddling across a big lake in a canoe with two older boys. I am in the bow, kneeling on the canoe's cedar ribs. We have been paddling for hours and my knees are numb and my shoulders ache with fatigue. Behind me, lashed to the midsection of the canoe, are two heavy, brown canvas packs holding our camping gear. There are three other canoes in the water beside us. My eyes are fixed on the far shore.

Just before noon we paddled through the narrows and turned southeast into the vastness of the lake. The map showed that to reach our destination we had to paddle six miles between two islands and a pair of long peninsulas reaching out from the mainland. When we started, the lake was flat calm. The wind picked up just after we passed the second island.

We are now out in the open lake, headed toward a thin blue shoreline more than two miles away. According to the counselor in the canoe beside us, the wind is blowing a steady 15 knots and gusting to 20. During the last half hour the waves have increased in size and their white-breaking crests now are higher than our canoes.

We are on the final day of a weeklong trip. A truck is waiting on the far shore to pick us up and drive us back to the camp. Less than an hour ago, we all made a decision. We decided that since the wind was directly behind us and we were paddling with the waves, we would push on.

Up ahead, everything is distance. When the waves began to build, every pleasure boat in sight headed toward land. If we get into trouble there would be no one to help us.

We are past the point where we can turn back. Our canoes keep hurrying forward, climbing up the backs of the waves, hesitating on their crests and then pitching down into the troughs in front of them. From my cramped position in the bow I can see everything: the rising blue-greenness, the glittering froth breaking apart, the bleak hollow of the troughs.

My body is humming with fear. My mind's eye sees the canoe catching a wave coming in from another direction, turning slowly on its side with the sky spinning overhead and the water rising all around, waves everywhere, packs floating, the canoe upside down and the other canoes unable to turn back into the concussion of the wind.

I picture the long, dark fathoms below us, the lake divided into chasm after chasm. I imagine I am down there, trapped in a place where lungs have no air.

I am on terms with death in the way all boys are, not knowing what it really means, having only seen it steal into the body of a caught fish, the flapping muscles slowing, the tail going lax, the bright look in the eyes becoming flat and milky.

But I know something about death from stories told of a father lost in the smoking crash of his aircraft a few months after his youngest son was born. The Second World War was imminent and Flying Officer MacInnis, an instructor in the Royal Canadian Air Force, had a student in the cockpit behind him when the fog slid in off Lake Ontario. They were approaching the airfield and had no instruments or air traffic controller to bring them down. As they searched for the runway, another aircraft slammed into theirs. Among the broken parts raining down on the earth were the bodies of four men. It happened the day my mother went to the airfield to watch her husband do the thing he loved most.

My father came from a family of poor Scottish immigrants who had sailed across the Atlantic in the 1800s. In Nova Scotia, they became farmer-fishermen who pulled nets, felled trees and plowed the wind-blasted soil. Searching for something more than this rote sameness, my father traveled west to McGill University in Montreal and then to the Air Force flight training school in Trenton, Ontario. He loved flying and soon became an instructor. When his burning aircraft fell out of the sky, he was 32.

I am on this lake because I love to paddle canoes, letting water take me where it will. Water thrills me. Its color and motion are irresistible. But now, inside the heave of these waves, I am learning that water has fearsome and unpredictable energies.

"That's a good rhythm, Joe. Stay with it," says the boy kneeling in the middle of the canoe behind me. Hugh is from northern Vermont. Bob Travis, the biggest and strongest of us, is in the stern trying to keep the canoe pointed in the right direction, straight downwind. Somehow all three of us have agreed telepathically that the big lake with its rows of foaming crests and obsidian depths has become a lethal threat. We do not talk about it. Our energies are focused on only one thing. Each stroke brings us closer to the shoreline.

Never have I been so dependent on two other people and never have they been so dependent on me. If I fail to match the rhythm of my stroke to the rhythm of the waves—I set the pace for the three of us—we might swamp. One mistake and we will be up to our necks in water.

But there is a part of me that is relishing this. Never have I been so physically and mentally attuned to the natural world. The big lake is tutoring me with its forces. I am 12 years old, discovering there is wisdom to be found in something both terrifying and beautiful.

I grew up in Toronto, on the north shore of Lake Ontario, the easternmost of the five Great Lakes. Standing at the edge of the lake, I fell under the spell of its long shoreline, the endless horizon and the timeless motion of its water. The big ships that sailed into and out of the harbor existed in a separate world, as remote as another planet.

At school, I was a lazy student fascinated with the maps on the wall that showed the uninhabited lands of northern Canada and the deep blue spaces in between the continents. Somehow I sensed that below the surface of the oceans was a multitude of living things, diving and darting, living and dying. It was an alien world I desperately wanted to explore.

In my first year of high school, after reading Jules Verne's *Twenty Thousand Leagues under the Sea,* the ocean became a place I could at least

GLEN
LOATES

A diver from Jules Verne's *Twenty Thousand Leagues under the Sea,* which was first
published in 1870. Still in print, the book has inspired countless young people,
including the author, to pursue careers in marine science and undersea exploration.
(Courtesy of Glen Loates)

imagine. *Twenty Thousand Leagues* is the fictional story of Professor Aronnax and two companions who spend 10 months with Captain Nemo on board his enormous submarine *Nautilus*. During their 40,000-mile undersea journey, they walk through coral gardens, recover sunken treasure and engage in hand-to-hand combat with a giant squid. According to Captain Nemo, "Man can live underwater, provided he can carry with him a sufficient supply of breathable air. While working underwater, a workman wears a waterproof garment, his head in a metal helmet, and he receives air from the outside by means of pumps equipped with proper controls."

An avid reader, I often re-read Verne's classic to join Professor Aronnax preparing to dive into the sea. He would step into a compartment inside *Nautilus,* in which diving suits were hanging on the wall, ready for use. As he describes it:

> Two members of the crew came to help us put on those heavy waterproof garments, made of seamless rubber and designed to withstand considerable pressure … the material of the tunic is stretched over bands of copper which crossed the chest, protecting it from the pressure of the water, and leaving the lungs free to breathe … the top part of our garment ended in a threaded copper collar upon which the metal helmet is screwed. Three holes, protected by thick glass, made it possible to see in every direction.

After suiting up with the professor, I joined him as he was ushered into the small chamber that allowed the divers to exit into the ocean.

> I heard a watertight door close behind us, and we were in total darkness. A few minutes later I heard a high-pitched hissing and I felt a cold sensation rising up from my feet to my chest. Obviously a valve had been turned inside the ship, letting in the water from the outside. We were soon immersed, and when the chamber was full, a second door on the side of the *Nautilus* opened. Something like a twilight appeared, and a moment later, our feet were touching the bottom of the sea.

What started as faint whisper in the ear about undersea exploration eventually led to my first scuba dive off the coast of Fort Lauderdale in Florida. I was 17 years old, and during that unforgettable hour I decided that diving was something I was going to do for the rest of my life. Two years later, I went to medical school to learn everything I could about the human body and how it adapted to strange environments. Finally, in my mid twenties, I found myself journeying to another country in search of an exalted form of work.

FOUR

OCTOBER 19, 1963. I turn the car away from the neon haze of the all-night diner and drive back onto the highway. Off to my left, a reef of pink clouds straddles the black crest of the Appalachian mountains. I am just outside of Scranton, Pennsylvania, heading south to Philadelphia. It is the dawn of a new day and my veins are flush with caffeine and the warmth of fortune's favor.

Two weeks ago, I had a phone call from Ed Link's sister, Marilyn. "I am happy to say," she said in a quiet voice, "that you have been awarded a Link Foundation Fellowship to study diving medicine at the University of Pennsylvania. Mr. Link will call you in a few days to outline how to divide your time between the university and the ship."

In the back seat of the car is a duffle bag full of clothes and a brief-case full of books. In my shirt pocket is my Canadian passport, an American immigration card and an American draft card. At nine o'clock tomorrow morning, I begin my first day of work at the Institute of Environmental Medicine.

Like most Canadians, I spend a lot of time trying to understand the huge republic lying to the south of my country. No other nation is so raucous in its culture, aggressive in its policies or inspiring in its humanities. Three years ago, during his inaugural address, President John F. Kennedy said his country was on the edge of "a New Frontier, the frontier of the 1960s, a frontier of uncommon opportunities and paths, a frontier of unfulfilled hopes and threats." And when he said, "ask not what your country can do for you, but what you can do for your country," I felt—although I am a Canadian—that he was talking to me.

Last January, Martin Luther King spoke in front of a huge crowd at the Lincoln Memorial in Washington. "I have a dream," he said. "I have a dream that one day, on the red hills of Georgia, sons of former slaves and the sons of former slave owners will be able to sit down together at the table of brotherhood." Two months ago, more than 200,000 Americans conducted a march on Washington to demonstrate their support for civil rights.

I look through the windshield at the sky turning red in the east. America is where the Europeans encountered an alien natural world and tamed it. For them, freedom was not in the confinement of settlements; it was out in the plains, under an endless sky. One becomes an American by turning one's back on security and lighting out into unknown territory.

I am aware of America's dark side. One month ago, a bomb exploded in a Birmingham church and killed four black Alabama school children. This is a nation where everything seems to revolve around the Cold War and the Bomb, the weapon that swallows cities. A month from now the open black limousine will ease down the sunny Dallas street crowded with people, the shots will ring out, and the people will gasp as the man's head in the back seat of the limousine jerks forward with the shearing of bone and tissue. I will be in Washington then, and the event will leave me lost in silence. For the first time in my life, I will discover there are forces in society that seem more powerful than the forces of nature.

The highway takes me deep inside the folded ridges of the Appalachians. The sun is just below the rimrock, throwing a faint yellow light into a line of clouds. On my right, behind a blur of trees, a river races through a valley. On both sides, the mountains are purple and black, with a white mist linking their crowns. These old hills have a distance and a stillness that sprawl back to the beginning of the earth.

❖

The University of Pennsylvania, established in Philadelphia in 1740 by Benjamin Franklin, is the oldest university in the United States. Its long list of distinguished professors and alumni includes seven of the men who signed the Declaration of Independence. Tagging along with a group of colorfully dressed students, I walk across Pine Street and through a high-arched brick gate into an esplanade of green lawns and dark red buildings. Five minutes later, I pass through the doorway of the first medical school in the 13 colonies.

Its interior is as gloomy as a bat cave. The walls of the main corridor are lined with portraits of old men radiating authority. I walk along the marble floor to the back of the building, find the sign that says Institute of Environmental Medicine and descend a flight of steel-edged stairs. The air smells faintly of formaldehyde.

The institute is a complex of offices and laboratories inhabited by quiet-spoken men wearing thick glasses. I locate the office with Dr. Christian J. Lambertsen printed on its glass-paneled door and knock gently. "Come in," says a firm voice.

Lambertsen stands up to shake my hand. He is tall, with square shoulders and thinning red hair. There is something about his stance and carriage that makes it easy to imagine him doing hard physical work.

His office is book-lined and orderly. On one side, a long desk holds stacks of scientific papers. Everything about the room says this is a man running an organization that produces serious scientists specializing in hard study and critical thinking.

When Lambertsen was my age, he was changing the shape of under-sea warfare. As a medical student, he developed a series of closed-circuit oxygen re-breathers for the military. Soon after, he began training the first U.S. combat swimmers. His work with underwater breathing systems, midget submarines and high explosives evolved into the tactics used by the U.S. Navy's underwater demolition teams.

For the next half hour, Lambertsen tells me about the institute's mission and where I fit into that mission. Ed Link has asked the institute to provide medical support for his next dive. Dr. Jim Dickson, a senior member of the staff, will work with me on the project. During the next few months, I will participate in diving research experiments at the institute and at the Navy's Experimental Diving Unit in Washington.

As Lambertsen speaks, a strange tension builds in my stomach. The institute is a crucible for rigorous learning. Given my inherent sloth and quick-order boredom, do I have the staying power for months of study, late-night experiments and dog-work weekends?

The professor's eyes lock onto mine. From what I've read and heard, Lambertsen has an encyclopedic knowledge of space and diving medicine coupled with a do-it-now attitude. He is an introspective thinker with a frontal curiosity. Just being in the same room with him, listening to the cadence of his carefully chosen words, makes me want to do everything I can to hurry his nation into its undersea future.

⋅⋰⋅

During the next six months, I settle into the rhythm of the institute, reading books, attending seminars, working on a high-pressure experiment in one of the smaller labs. Dickson takes me to U.S. Navy facilities in Washington and New London and introduces me to the leading naval scientists, including Dr. George Bond. In the process, I give myself up willingly to the sacrifices of turning into a physician-scientist. I also try to get a sense of the bigger picture by studying the geography of the continental shelves and finding out why it is so important to learn how to "live" and work on them.

The continental shelves start at the coastline of the continents and range out as far as several hundred miles. They are generally flat, sometimes carved by undersea canyons and covered with as much as 600 feet of water. Their submergence is due to a dramatic change in sea level: with the melting of the mile-high glaciers of the last Ice Age, the ocean's basins were filled to overflowing and salt water slowly spilled over the seaward edge of all the world's coasts. With an area of ten million square miles—the size of Europe and South America combined—the shelves belong more to the continents than to the oceans. Their basement rock is continental granite and is covered with sediments rather than deep-ocean abyssal ooze.

Mineral deposits similar to those on dry land have been discovered on the continental shelves. The most important is oil, the steaming blood

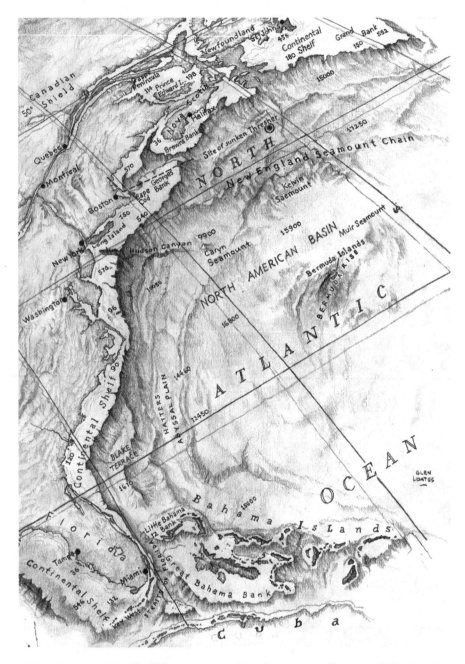

The Continental Shelf off the east coast of North America. *(Courtesy of Glen Loates)*

of the earth, made out of the massive dying of ancient animals and plants. In 1963, the oil industry spent $5 billion to locate and recover oil on the continental shelves in the Gulf of Mexico, the Persian Gulf and the North Sea.

Starting in the 1940s, with a shallow well in Louisiana, oil companies began punching holes in the bedrock of the continental shelves. Now their drill pipes are boring through as much as 250 feet of water before descending into the sediments. Acoustic surveys of the seabed confirm enormous hydrocarbon reservoirs at much greater depths.

A team of six or seven commercial divers is essential to the day-to-day operation of an offshore drilling platform. If there is a problem on the seafloor with the drill pipe or blowout-preventor—a collection of valves and pipes two stories high and designed to control the sudden increase in pressure if the drill pipe hits a pocket of oil or gas—divers are sent down to fix it. The oil companies reason that if divers could work deeper and stay longer under the ocean, the companies could drill right out to the edge of the continental shelf.

Unfortunately, there are many hazards inhibiting easy access to the depths, including hypothermia, nitrogen narcosis and decompression sickness. These give rise to challenging medical questions. How deep can divers go before their bodies fail them? What stresses will prevent divers from doing productive work at extreme depths?

In 1957, a charismatic U.S. Navy physician, Captain George Bond, started seeking answers to these questions. In a series of dives in a compression chamber at the Naval Medical Research Laboratory in New London, Bond exposed small animals to a pressure of 200 feet. Then a group of volunteer Navy divers lived for a week under the same precisely controlled conditions of pressure, temperature and humidity. The experiments confirmed that humans could breathe helium instead of nitrogen for long periods without ill effects. It was Bond's work that encouraged Ed Link to carry out his first long-duration dive.

Link's first experiment took place in the Mediterranean Sea on the French Riviera. In September 1962, Robert Stenuit, a young Belgian diver, climbed into Link's submersible decompression chamber and locked the hatch behind him. The sealed chamber was lifted by *Sea Diver*'s crane and lowered into the water beside the ship. Stenuit helped guide the aluminum chamber to a depth of 200 feet and remained there for 24 hours, swimming out into the water to work and returning to the chamber to rest. During the dive he breathed the same oxy-helium mixture as the men in Bond's experiment. When the dive was over, Stenuit avoided hours of hanging on a line decompressing in the cold water. Instead, he secured himself inside the chamber and was hoisted to the deck of *Sea Diver*, where he was decompressed in safety and relative comfort.

Along the same Mediterranean coast, the French undersea pioneer Jacques Cousteau was also initiating experiments to allow humans to live inside the ocean. The first dive in his *Conshelf* project took place in the shallow waters near Marseille in September 1962. Two men lived at 35 feet for a week, working in the sea several hours a day, returning to a cylindrical cabin to eat and sleep.

The following summer, Cousteau's group established an underwater settlement at the remote Sha'ab Rumi Reef in the Red Sea. "Starfish House," an assembly of cylindrical chambers placed in 33 feet of water, was home to five men for a month. Nearby was a structure that housed a small sub whose pilot and observer made dives as deep as 1,000 feet. Down the slope from Starfish House, at a depth of 85 feet, two men lived in the oxygen-helium-nitrogen atmosphere of their "deep cabin" for seven days, making short excursions as deep as 360 feet.

Link and Cousteau had made a significant start, but if humans were to live under the sea at depths of 200 feet and beyond, many medical-engineering questions had to be answered. What new equipment must be developed to make it possible to breathe easily and stay warm at great depths? What kind of structures had to be built to provide safe shelter on the deep edge of the continental shelf? With the support of the U.S. Navy and practical men such as Chris Lambertsen, Ed Link was determined to find the answers.

The tall window above my desk frames a dark sky filled with snow flurries and a slick concrete sidewalk empty of students. Streetlights glimmer. The trees in front of the next building look like thin strands of black coral.

The long wooden workbench in front of me is strewn with vise-grips, screwdrivers, adjustable wrenches, a tape recorder, notebooks and a small, cylindrical high-pressure chamber. The bench also holds a paramagnetic oxygen analyzer and an infrared carbon dioxide analyzer, which are measuring the concentrations of gas inside the chamber. Oxygen and helium high-pressure cylinders are lashed together on the floor beside me. Thin coils of copper piping run from their control valves into the side of the chamber.

I peer through the chamber's view port. In the glow of a tiny light-bulb, eight white mice, dazed by the unexpected pressure, stand in separate cubicles. Their eyes are closed and they are trembling and gasping for breath.

I feel a kind of desperate elation. It has taken me a month of planning, two weeks of preparation and more than three hours of precision compression and gas analysis to compress them to a simulated depth of 4,000 feet. If they were under the ocean, they would be almost halfway to the depth of *Thresher*. No air-breathing, land-living animals have ever been this deep.

Our experiment is designed to explore the limits of tolerance of small animals to extreme pressures. We are looking for answers to two essential questions. Are animals (and perhaps humans) able to breathe at 4,000 feet, and what is the effect of such pressure on their central nervous systems? The simulated dive is also testing the new oxygen and carbon dioxide analyzers we will use during Link's next dive.

I study the condition of each mouse and make the following entry in my journal. "At 1930 hours the mice were under a pressure of almost 1,800 pounds per square inch. All eight appear wobbly-legged, but are moving about. They are having difficulty breathing."

I try to imagine the atmosphere inside the chamber. It is mostly helium with a trace of nitrogen and oxygen. The helium has been added because at depths greater than about 100 feet nitrogen becomes narcotic.

Nitrogen makes up almost 79 percent of normal air. Although it does not affect the human body at sea level, it has an anesthetic effect under pressure. At depths greater than 100 feet, nitrogen molecules flood the brain and diminish a diver's physical and mental abilities. The condition is called nitrogen narcosis, or "rapture of the deep." Helium is much less narcotic and easier to breathe at great depths.

I look at the mice and feel a shiver of guilt. They are involuntarily participating in a dive because we need critical information about living at high pressure. They are breathing hesitantly, drawing in the metallic air and letting it out at short intervals, their lives hanging on every breath.

They will remain at this pressure for the next four hours. I am grateful to them because they have helped us confirm that small animal exposure to this depth is not lethal and the narcotic effect of helium is not incapacitating. At the end of the four hours, it will be my responsibility, over a period of 15 hours, to decompress them carefully back to the surface.

❖

At 6:00 A.M., when I look inside the chamber, my heart sinks. Three of the mice have stopped breathing and are lying against the sides of their cubicles, their legs rigid. Since midnight I have been carrying out a precise decompression schedule, carefully venting the chamber, bringing the mice back to the surface at a rate of four feet per minute. I've monitored two pressure gauges, keeping one hand on a stopwatch and the other on a flow meter. Every 15 minutes I checked the oxygen and carbon dioxide concentrations and made an entry in my notebook. In spite of my obsessive attention to detail, three mice have died.

The depths of the ocean contain monsters and one of them is pressure. It killed *Thresher* and it killed the mice by invading their cells and waiting for the moment to attack.

I check and recheck every part of the experiment—the chamber, the piping and the analyzers. The one thing I can't verify is what destruction the shifting molecules of gas inflicted on the mice. All I know is that somewhere within their complex network of cells, microscopic bubbles formed and blood stopped flowing to vital tissues.

It suddenly dawns on me that I may be responsible for all this. What have I done this time that is different from other trials at shallower depths? Then I remember the shortcut. Usually, a few hours before the start of compression, I feed the mice, getting them ready for their long ordeal. On this dive, because I was short of food pellets, I gave a leaf of lettuce to three of them. Perhaps the lettuce caused gas to form in their stomachs, gas that expanded and set off a chain of events. If the mice had been human divers, I would be sending out for body bags.

Whatever the reason, the three fatalities are my first lesson in diving medicine: it takes only one small, stupid mistake to wipe out a hundred well-done tasks.

FIVE

MARCH 1964. On a sunny afternoon just before Easter, I pick up Route 1 in Miami, turn south and drive down a thin ribbon of blacktop toward the ocean. Thirty miles later, the road leaves the mainland and passes through swamp grass and mangroves until it arrives at a long, flat island. Beyond thick groves of palm trees, a huge plain of dark blue water runs out to the horizon. I am in the upper Florida Keys. For the next two hours, I drive across 41 emerald-green islands and over a series of steel-and-concrete bridges, until the road runs out in Key West.

As soon as I enter the old town, with its shady streets and wood frame houses, I head toward the intersection of Whitehead and South Streets. I park the car and walk toward a low seawall overlooking the ocean. I am alone except for a pair of man-of-war birds riding the thermals overhead. According to the map, this is the southernmost point of the continental United States.

The tide is out and a southerly breeze carries the aroma of drying seaweed. I take off my shoes, climb over the seawall and step into the water. It is almost as warm as my skin. In the depths an arm's-length away are a pair of striped yellow fish and a cluster of purple sea fans. The floor of the sea slopes steadily downward into a place that has never known sunlight. Its hidden sediments and sand run out to the horizon, and out to the next horizon and the next. I am perched on the edge of the greatest wilderness on the planet.

To the north and west lies the Gulf of Mexico, a 600,000-square-mile basin of the Atlantic Ocean almost enclosed by the United States and Mexico. Its widest continental shelves, sometimes more than 250 miles across, are off the shores of Florida, Louisiana, Texas and Mexico's Yucatan peninsula. To the south is the Caribbean Sea, its one million square miles enclosed by Central America, South America and a curving arc of islands. Most of the Caribbean's continental shelves are narrow and drop off quickly into deep water.

A line of puffy white clouds lies on top of a horizon as straight as a ruler. Beneath the clouds runs the Gulf Stream, the great blue river that cools the shores of Yucatan and then courses thousands of miles along the east coat of North America before it crosses the Atlantic to warm the fjords of Norway. Its indigo depths hold a volume of water equal to the flow of 3,000 Mississippis, and within its crosscurrents, eddies and meanders are uncounted creatures including bluefin tuna, mako sharks, swordfish and blue marlin.

Beyond the clouds, only 90 miles away, is Cuba, where 16 months ago American surveillance aircraft discovered Soviet missiles armed with nuclear warheads. Fourteen Soviet ships with additional missiles were en route to the island. President Kennedy sent Strategic Air Command bombers loaded with H-bombs aloft to circle the Mediterranean Sea and the Arctic Ocean, and ordered his fleet of nuclear submarines to be on full alert. He imposed air and sea quarantines around Cuba and insisted that Moscow withdraw its missiles. For 13 days, millions of people held their breath as Kennedy and Khrushchev shook the nuclear dice. Finally, the Russian bear turned his ships around and took his warheads home.

As I am climbing back over the seawall, the air begins to vibrate, a scream rises out of the ocean and a pair of silver Navy jets slash across the sky heading north.

That night I take a long walk, strolling through the narrow streets and laneways, trying to inhale the history, romance, sexuality and danger of the small island floating on the very edge of America. Near the two-story house where Hemingway once lived are sidewalks uprooted by the roots of strangler figs. I pass a line of moored shrimp boats, their decks empty of men, long V nets streaming down from their booms, numerous sea creatures stranded in their webs. The air smells of tidal flats and turtle grass. Sloppy Joe's Bar is on a corner with two sides open to the night breeze. I take a seat next to a man in cut-off jeans and sandals, and order a Bacardi neat. His name is Mel and he is a shrimp fisherman whose trawler is in the yard for repairs. His family is from Mexico and he's been working on the boats for 20 years. Like most people who call this place home, he is fascinated with the history of Key West, or Cayo Hueso, as the Spaniards call it. This island has always been an outpost, he tells me. First came the pirates and the wreckers, men who used lights to draw vessels onto the reefs so they could make off with their cargos. The U.S. Navy came here during the Civil War with a fleet of wooden-hulled ships and have maintained a base ever since. Sea turtles and sponges made Key West an industrial island for a time, until too many fishermen put down too many nets and emptied the sea. As Mel talks, a cockroach circles the heel of his sandal searching for whatever delicacy he's brought in from the deck of his shrimp boat.

I ask him how shrimp fishing got started. In the late 1940s, he tells me, Navy divers on maneuvers found swarms of "pink gold," the night-crawling gulf shrimp. Suddenly, fishermen had another new frontier. "Went like gangbusters for more than ten years," he says. "And then it collapsed. Once again, too many boats and too many nets." He glances at a black-and-white photograph of Hemingway on the wall and throws back a shot of tequila.

"But now we're gettin' a new product out of the sea. Square grouper," he says with a grin.

Grouper are big fish that live on the reefs, but this is a variety I don't recognize. "Square grouper?" I say. "Never heard of them."

"Hang around this town long enough an' you will, my fren'," he says with a huge smile. "It's the golden weed—marijuana—and it comes in neatly tied bales. You don't need no net. You don't need no hooks. All you need is an amigo in South America and a lot of *cojones*."

❖

The next morning I drive down to the naval station that occupies the entire southwest end of the island. During the Civil War, the station became known as "the Gibraltar of America." In the Second World War there were as many as 30 big ships berthed in its wide harbor and 15,000 sailors stationed here.

I turn on to Southard Street, drive one block and stop at the white guard shack just inside the main gate. A large black man with spit-polished boots and a freshly pressed uniform steps out of the booth and approaches my car. The letters M.P. are stamped in white paint across the front of his gleaming metal helmet. I open my window.

"Yes, sir," he says.

"I'm Dr. Joe MacInnis and I'm reporting for work on the research vessel *Sea Diver*."

His eyes narrow and he looks through the window at my T-shirt and jeans.

"Are you a civilian?"

"Yes, sir."

He leans over and looks in the back seat at my large duffle bag. When his eyes return to mine they are dark and hard.

"What is the research vessel *Sea Diver*?"

I tell him that *Sea Diver* is Edwin Link's ship and she has been assigned a berth at the station for the next three months and that I am reporting for duty as the ship's doctor. "Pull over here and wait," he says.

I turn into the parking area and shut off the engine. Two cars pull up to the guard shack and the M.P. waves them through. Then he steps into the shack and picks up the phone. While he is talking he keeps looking in my direction. "Yes sir," I hear him say, "he's a civilian."

The military aircraft comes in low with a hideous sound, its delta wings carrying racks of nested rockets on both sides, its engines spouting spikes of flame. I can see the control flaps working the air, keeping the big machine level. It is flying south, trailing twin smoke trails of noise behind it.

The M.P. comes out of the shack and stands beside the car. "Can I see some I.D.?"

I hand him my passport. He looks at its cover, turns its pages and then stares at me.

"It says that you are a Canadian."

"Yes, sir."

"Are you aware that this is an American base?"

"I am, sir."

"Have you any orders assigning you to this base?"

"No, sir." I feel the color draining out of my face. In desperation I open my briefcase and reach for an envelope. "Perhaps this might help explain things." My hands are shaking.

The M.P. opens the envelope and studies my green immigration card. Then he takes a long look at my American draft card. When I applied for work in the United States, I was informed that because America was at war in Vietnam, I could be called up for active duty on short notice.

He asks me about the work being done on *Sea Diver*. I explain that I am joining a team preparing for the longest deep dive ever made, part of a program to improve the Navy's ability to work deep under the ocean. He studies my face for a long time, hands me the cards and waves me forward.

Beyond the main gate is a sprawling collection of barracks, cargo cranes, docks, storage sheds and workshops. In a large open drill field between the buildings, a squad of men wearing shorts and T-shirts are running in place and chanting in cadence. The streets are filled with sailors in white uniforms.

The guard has instructed me to follow the road as it winds around the waterfront until I reach the outer pier on the far side of the harbor. I drive between a high gray water tower and a two-floor machine shop. The air is filled with dust, humidity and diesel exhaust. As I turn left at the waterfront, I see two long, gray submarines lying in the calm water beside their supply ships. From the decks of the ships come the hiss of compressed air and the sound of chippers and grinders.

Sea Diver is tied up inside the wide concrete jetty that guards the harbor. Her white hull paint is stained with rust and her deck is cluttered with fuel drums, anchor chains and a cluster of orange high-pressure helium gas cylinders. On the jetty next to her are stacks of wooden crates and empty pallets. I park the car and spend a few minutes studying the small knot of men lowering something off the stern with the ship's boom crane.

Taking a deep breath, I make my way across the jetty and up the steel gangway onto *Sea Diver*'s deck. The men at the crane glance over with an air of suspicion and return to their work. Finally, one of them lays down his tools, walks over to where I am standing and takes off his sunglasses. He has brown eyes and a small, well-trimmed mustache and is wearing a black nylon bathing suit.

"I'm Robert Stenuit," he says with a soft French accent, "the project's chief diver. You must be Dr. MacInnis. We've been expecting you."

I spend the rest of the afternoon watching the ship's crew work, trying to understand the dynamics of lifting lead weights into a large tray, slinging the tray with canvas webbing and lowering the whole assembly carefully into the water beside the ship. The men curse lightly and laugh loudly. Occasionally, they look at the stranger standing on the far side of the deck. I have the feeling that they perceive the new arrival has lots of book learning, but knows nothing about wire rope, running rigging or seamanship. On an oil-glazed deck, with heavy loads under tension, I am a hazard to my own health.

In the evening, I quietly stow my gear in the small two-bunk cabin up forward and then take a long walk along the length of the jetty. A line of low, green islands lies to the west. In the sunset, *Sea Diver* is almost pink, the smallest vessel in the harbor. I turn to watch the sun slowly slice into the pale curve of the sea until a final red flame crests the horizon and disappears.

During the next few weeks, I struggle to become part of the confederation of men working on *Sea Diver*. I discover that on a small ship everyone depends on everyone else. When there is work to be done, from cleaning the gear to unloading a truckload of boxes, everyone pitches in. Because the ship's rooms are so confining and there is such limited space in the corridors, everyone is especially polite and considerate. I learn how to choose my words carefully and listen hard before offering a suggestion. I also learn to look for the humor that lies inside every task.

As the weeks pass, I begin to use my medical skills. I treat a hand burned on a steam pipe in the engine room. I put a cast on a wrist fractured in a fall on the rain-slicked deck. Most importantly, I pay close attention when a crew member talks about the stress of his job or tells me about a problem he is having with his girl back home. In time, I begin to earn the confidence of the men on the ship.

I take a particular interest in the divers, especially Robert Stenuit, one of the men making the deep dive. One night, Dan Eden, the ship's chief engineer, tells me what he knows about the soft-spoken Belgian. Eden is a chain-smoking Englishman, the kind of man who can sniff the air and know exactly where to squirt a few drops of oil on an overheating generator. He is also the kind of man who quickly detects the flaw in a shipmate's character. I ask him how long he has known Stenuit.

"About three years," he tells me. "He's a salvage expert and under-water archeologist. Since Captain Link brought him on board, he's had an untiring commitment to the project. He's a loyal friend. And one of the bravest men I've ever met."

I have been intrigued with Stenuit since the first day we met, trying to assess his strengths and weaknesses. His love of books and hard toil on deck tell me that he is a man who moves easily between physical and mental worlds. Beneath his shyness is a sense of purpose as solid as a marlinspike. To sustain Link's confidence, he does exactly what he is asked and works twice as hard as anyone else. I have followed his example since the day we first met.

One day Stenuit takes me aside to advise me on the delicate protocol of working with Ed Link. "Ed's got diabetes," he says, "so don't discuss anything serious with him before breakfast. Until his blood sugar is up, he is easily irritated. Listen hard to what he says before you offer advice. Remember that he's smarter than all of us put together. When you think you are right, find a way to make him think that your idea is his idea." He thinks for a few seconds and adds, "For Americans, ownership is everything."

One of my favorite places on *Sea Diver* is the small laboratory-workshop just aft of the engine room. When one steps inside its confined, well-lit space and closes its heavy steel hatch, the heat and clamor of a working ship are sealed off. This room, with its deep closets and wide shelves, is where we store our diving suits and breathing regulators. On one side are a workbench, a row of bookshelves and a generous supply of electrical outlets. It is a good place to go if I need a haven for study.

Late one night, I am in the lab reading the technical manual for a new gas analyzer. The Beckman Company in California has asked us to test a prototype with unique electronic circuits that will give a direct reading of the oxygen and carbon dioxide levels inside the station. If it works, it will be a crucial step in allowing divers to be independent of the surface.

Convinced that a committee of six blind men who despise clarity wrote the manual, I am having difficulty understanding its arcane language. I press on, aware that two men's lives may depend on how much I know. As I turn the pages, I hear the sound of an approaching thunderstorm through the hull plates beside me.

There is a quiet knock from across the room, the hatch swings inward, and Stenuit steps through the opening.

"Oh, I'm sorry," he says, "I didn't know anyone was here. I didn't mean to disturb you."

"Not at all. Come in. At this point I'd welcome any distraction from this."

I point to the manual and the small stainless-steel analyzer lying on the workbench. About the size of a coffee can, it has two small dials on one end and a large, round screw on the other. Stenuit walks over to the bench, picks it up with both hands and holds it out at arm's length. "Have you any idea how much this cost?" he asks.

"It's a prototype, so I guess it cost a lot. More than your salary and my Link Foundation fellowship combined."

"I was curious," he says, "so I weighed it. At current market prices it's worth its weight in sixteenth-century gold coins."

We talk for a while about the amount of money being poured into the program by Link and a number of large institutions, including the National Geographic Society and the U.S. Navy. We agree that Link is one of the few men with the skill and reputation to bring all the partners together. He is also the only man we know for whom making money and creating jobs are only part of a well-lived life. In his late fifties, when most men are heading for retirement, Link is still searching for new challenges.

The deep booming of the thunderstorm is almost on top of the ship. We stop to listen as the first raindrops hammer the steel deck overhead. The lights in the room dim and then brighten.

During the past months, Jim Dickson and I have put Stenuit through every possible medical examination. He has been probed and prodded like a Christmas turkey. Vials of blood were taken from both arms and he has been X-rayed from his cranium to his metatarsals. As I studied the results of the tests, it occurred to me that I knew almost everything about his anatomy and physiology but very little about what was going on inside his head. I need to know if he will stay calm throughout the dive and maintain this calm in an emergency. If he has to abandon the station, will he focus on the problem or will he panic? Does his gentle insouciance hide fear, fearlessness or something in between?

As the storm moves off, I edge into the subject by asking what he thinks is the most serious hurdle he will face at 400 feet. Is it keeping warm in the frigid water? Is it trying to talk when he is out of breath and his lungs are filled with oxy-helium?

"It is neither," he says softly. "At this time, our biggest hurdle is the final assembly of the breathing gear that will allow us to work outside the station."

We are working on a project where fear is always present but never discussed. I suspect that Stenuit is one of those men whose fear—and courage—is hidden beneath his commitment and resolve.

A week ago, I supervised his first overnight stay in Link's new undersea station. The station is an inflatable black rubber tent, seven and a half feet long and four feet in diameter. It is held to the bottom of the harbor by six tons of lead ballast. Inside are two small view ports, a pair of steel-frame bunks and, in the center of the floor, a round access well. To get into it, a diver stands on the ballast tray, slips off his diving gear and pulls himself up through the well to the level of the floor.

The brief shallow-water test exposed serious flaws in our equipment. The seams in the rubber walls of the station leaked a continuous stream of air. During the last hours of Stenuit's stay, the carbon dioxide scrubber failed and left him, quite literally, out of breath. He emerged from his brief sojourn joking about a series of unexplained short circuits in the electrical system. "They made my hair stand on end," he said. "Add a few more volts, give me some chest paddles and if I go into cardiac arrest, I can restart my heart."

The thunder has stopped. As Stenuit picks up his things, I try once again to get him to talk about his feelings. I ask him if he was frightened during his prolonged 200-foot dive in the Mediterranean. He does not answer right away.

"A little fear goes a good long way," he says finally, with a smile. "Intelligent fear takes the pressure off your luck and your courage."

SIX

MY TEMPORARY RESIDENCE in Key West is the Santa Maria, a tan-colored, low-rent motel on East Simonton Street. It has a small, rust-stained swimming pool surrounded by stunted coconut palms. My room smells of chlorine and cigar smoke. Its thin walls allow me to share the nightly Bible service of my next-door neighbors, a Baptist couple from Alabama.

Early one Saturday morning, I slide out of bed in the humid darkness and slip into my shorts. Link wants us on the ship at sun-up for a pressure test of the undersea station and submersible decompression chamber. We have placed the station on the bottom of the harbor and connected its high-pressure hoses and communication cables to the chamber on the deck of *Sea Diver*. We will slowly increase the pressure on the whole system, searching its network of hoses, cables and fittings for the flaw that might invite disaster at 400 feet. We are also going to run a 24-hour test of our redesigned carbon dioxide scrubber.

I step outside into the damp night air and unlock my bicycle. I switch on its handlebar light and start to pedal along Simonton Street. The street is empty except for a dark blue garbage truck with music from Radio Free Habana spilling out its window. The sign on its back says "We Cater to Weddings." I pedal slowly, trying to wake up, my mind focused on the mug of black coffee waiting for me on *Sea Diver*.

I turn left on Southland Street. A hint of light has appeared in the eastern sky. I start to pedal faster to increase the breeze on my skin. As I approach the intersection at Duval Street, I stop pedaling. The light is red, but if I coast, I will arrive after it turns green.

I am just entering the intersection when I see a single headlight closing in from my right. The motorcycle doesn't stop. It speeds up, passes in front of me, brakes hard, strikes the sidewalk and then falls over on its side. There is the sound of glass breaking. "Oh, shit," says a voice aimed at me. "Goddamn asshole."

I stop and get off my bike. The light overhead is still green. My mouth is dry and my heart is hammering.

"What the fuck you doin'?" The man has short arms, a thick chest and a neck that seems a foot wide. His T-shirt is torn at the sleeve; an anchor and a pair of dolphins are tattooed on his right bicep. Everything about him, especially the booze on his breath, gives off the whiff of trouble.

"I'm sorry," I say, "but you came through ..."

He looks up at the light that has now turned red and then down at the broken glass that was once a bottle of Bacardi. Gleaming fingers of rum stream past his shoes into the gutter. "You ran the light, you mutha, and broke my best friend."

He closes his eyes, compresses his lips and reaches down to pick up his bike. Its front wheel is still spinning. As he stands up his entire body seems to collapse before he can right himself.

"We gotta go," he says to the bike. "We gotta get to the party." He turns the motorcycle in my direction and gets on. Using his feet to push forward, he steers around the broken bottle until his face is an arm's-length away. There is an S-shaped scar on his forehead. His eyes bore into my face as though he's looking through a sniper's night scope. Then he roars off toward the east. I shake my head and get back on my bicycle. It's a long time before I lose the feeling that I'm living in a town in which there is someone who wouldn't mind killing me.

❖

Some weeks later, I put on my scuba gear and slip into the water off the stern of *Sea Diver*. I let my eyes adjust and look around the misty depths of the harbor until I see the black rubber shape of the undersea station. Slowly I drop down until I am level with its open access well. I take a quick look at the ballast tray full of lead shot, which keeps the station anchored to the seafloor.

I ease my head up out of the water into the compressed air of the station and take a short, shallow breath. The air, at the same pressure as the water that surrounds it, tastes like a root cellar. A hissing sound coming from a rubber hose confirms my colleagues have started the low-pressure compressor on *Sea Diver*. In a few minutes the interior will fill with fresh air.

I shrug off my scuba gear and place it on the ballast tray below. Then I carefully pull myself up through the access well and position myself on the curved rubber floor. The water flowing off my wet suit into the well makes a muted, hollow sound.

A soft, green glow streaming through the two small view ports bathes everything in a shadowless light. Two pipe-frame bunks laced with canvas are above my head. The upper one holds a damp towel, a first aid kit and a radio intercom connected to *Sea Diver*.

This morning I told my shipmates that I wanted to make a dive to check the contents of the first aid kit, but my real reason for coming is to spend more time inside the station. I want to have a three-dimensional sense of the confined space that will be inhabited by Stenuit and his companion.

Even with one person inside, there isn't much room. With two people and all their gear, it is going to be like a fat couple camping in the back seat of a Volkswagen. I look down the access well into a ring of clear water. Fortunately, a lot of equipment can be stored a few feet away in pressure-proof steel canisters on top of the ballast tray.

When both men are in here with their life-support systems, extra clothing, diving equipment, a closed-circuit television camera and a communication system, it will take a ballerina's coordination to move without bumping into something. I run my fingers up the curving rubber wall. If something goes terribly wrong, like a sudden loss of pressure, there might be some high-octane panic trying to get out of here.

I hear a clicking sound followed by static. Someone on the surface has turned on the communication system.

"Doc, are you there? If you are, get back to the ship as soon as possible. There's been an accident."

As I drop down into the access well and slide on my scuba gear, I wonder what might be waiting for me on the surface. A dislocated shoulder? A crushed finger? During the past two months I've discovered that being on a ship means working with powerful machinery, high-pressure steam, heavy lifts and stepped-up electrical voltages. It's easy to lacerate your scalp because you didn't duck going through a steel doorway. It's simple to get your fingers caught in a winch. One slip on an oily deck and your skin is tight against a steam line and sizzling like bacon fat.

Exhaling carefully, I ascend through the water and surface at *Sea Diver*'s stern. At the top of the boarding ladder, Dan Eden helps me off with my gear.

"It's the captain," he says. "He's cut his hand working on the lathe." I follow Eden across the deck and down a ladder into the hot confines of the engine room. We make our way through a noisy tangle of boilers, pumps and pipes to where Ed Link is sitting on a stool in front of a lathe. Its rotating shaft holds a cylinder of heavy-gauge metal. The floor and the workbench in front of it are covered with steel shavings. A ragged cloth, red along its edges, is wrapped around Link's right hand. As I approach, he looks up and grins meekly.

"It's nothing," he says, "just a small cut."

"Can I take a look?"

"Sure. Go ahead. Really, it's nothing."

Kneeling down beside him I gently lift the edge of the makeshift bandage. Blood wells up from a jagged incision at the base of his thumb. Sticking out of one end of the sliced skin is the curled tip of a steel shaving. The master of the ship has given himself a non-lethal but serious wound that is probably infected.

"Well, sir," I say, "we have two choices. I can take you over to the Naval Hospital or I can treat you here." Uncertain about the depth of the incision or the microbes that may have gained access to its interior, I am hoping he will choose the first option.

The smile slips off Link's face and his eyes narrow. "When we're away from this harbor and on the open sea we won't have the luxury of choice. I suggest that you treat it right here. Right now. Then I can get back to work."

As I stand up, I notice Eden and Link exchange a look. The two men have worked together on *Sea Diver* for years, sailing her through a wilderness of wind and water. To them a ship is a place where every problem, no matter how difficult, is solved by a shipmate.

Working quickly, I place a clean towel on a table next to the ship's galley. After washing my hands, I unwrap Link's bandage and place his hand, palm up, on a sterile towel in the center of the table. Bright red blood oozes out of a long laceration between his wrist and his thumb.

"I am going to clean the wound thoroughly and then it's going to take a couple of stitches to close it. I'd like to give you a local anesthetic."

"That won't be necessary," says Link in a low voice. "I've had a lot worse than this. Just clean it, stitch it, and let me get back to the lathe."

I wash the skin around the wound with soap and water and then use sterile tweezers to tease the metal shaving from the torn tissue. As I do this, Link takes off his glasses with his other hand and places them on the table. There is a thin line of sweat on his forehead. After I remove the shaving and lay it on a towel, Link stares at the red, swollen area where it came from.

"What muscle is that?" he asks.

"The abductor," I answer. "The abductor brevis. It helps us oppose our thumbs. It's one of those muscles that enabled us to come out of the trees and begin making tools."

As I flush out the interior of the wound, Link holds up his other hand and begins looking at it, as if for the first time.

"Your thumb," I say, "has three bones and two joints. Concentric layers of muscles and tissue surround them. Fortunately, you did not sever the main artery or nerve."

Link is not listening. He is slowly rotating his hand in front of his face as if trying to figure out the inner workings of a device he has never noticed before.

"So these are the tools that make the tools," he says quietly. Then he looks at me and the sterile needle and thread I am going to use to stitch together his torn skin.

"How long before I can get back to work?"

"It would be best if you gave your hand a complete rest for 24 hours. If not, you might reopen the wound. And there's the risk of infection."

"I've got a job to do," says Link. "Fix me up so I can finish it." His voice is cool and distant. This is not a man to listen to a doctor's warning about a possible abscess.

I look across the table at Eden for support. He just shakes his head and smiles.

"OK. I'll add some extra thickness to your bandage and give you some antibiotics."

"You can save the antibiotics for someone else," Link says, giving me a look that says there will be no further discussion on the matter.

As I prepare the bandage, Link slowly extends his free arm out toward the middle of the table, keeping his elbow higher than his hand. Then he wraps his fingers and thumb around the rim of a coffee cup and picks it up. As he does this, his eyes follow the line from his shoulder to his elbow to his wrist and back again. He looks across the table at Eden.

"After we finish the deep dive," he says, "we're going to build a new crane. It's not going to be stiff like a boom crane. It's going to have the strength and flexibility of the human arm. It's going to reach down and pick things directly out of the water."

Link is talking about a technical challenge that has dogged him ever since he began lifting his two-ton submersible chamber into and out of the ocean. As soon as a heavy load breaks the surface, it starts swaying with the rhythm of the waves. With each roll of the ship the swaying increases. It takes at least four men with handling lines to lift the chamber up to the deck using *Sea Diver's* rigid boom crane. If the wind is up and the seas are running, the chamber becomes a two-ton wrecking ball. Like many self-taught men, Link has the ability to solve a problem by stepping to one side and looking at it from a different angle. This time he finds his solution by mimicking nature.

With eight carefully placed stitches, Link's wound is closed. During the entire procedure, he doesn't flinch or speak. His mind is elsewhere, wrestling with a logistical or engineering problem.

I secure the last knot and look down at Ed Link's hands. These are the hands that steered dozens of ships and aircraft and built the Link trainer.

"You finished?" he asks.

"Yes, sir."

He looks down at the row of stitches. "Nice job," he says with a smile. "I'll try not to mess it up."

❖

It is our last Saturday night in Key West before we leave for Miami, and we are drinking our way down Duval Street, sauntering from Dirty Harry's to the Bull and Whistle, knocking back full pitchers of cold beer, listening to the wail of amped-up Dylan songs, surrounded by a mob of off-duty sailors, bearded shrimp fishermen and a few wild-eyed crazies smoking hand-rolled cigarettes that smell like dirt after a hard rain.

Eight of us started out on this alcoholic ramble, but after midnight our number dropped to three. Apart from me, the two left are Art Noble, a muscular young deckhand who works for Dan Eden, and Bates Littlehales, a handsome staff photographer from *National Geographic,* who has been on the ship for a month taking pictures for Ed Link's next article. Both Art and Bates seem unaffected by the imposing amount of suds we are consuming.

Our last stop is at Captain Tony's, the oldest bar in town. In the 1930s, this dark, low-ceilinged hangout was the original Sloppy Joe's, Hemingway's favorite watering hole. It was owned by Joe Russell, a local charter boat captain who frequently took Hemingway deep-sea fishing.

One side of the saloon is open to the street. We spot an empty table and make our way past a row of crew-cut Marines sitting at the bar where Hemingway first saw the ravishing journalist Martha Gellhorn in 1937.

We are well oiled, but that doesn't stop us from ordering another round of beer with vodka chasers. Hanging on the wall next to our table are framed quotations. One of them is a scrap of wisdom from the bar's owner: "All you need in life is a tremendous sex drive and an enormous ego—brains don't mean a shit.—Captain Tony."

"I think I'm gonna take that back to the ship and hang it up in the engine room," says Noble. His voice has a strange muted sound to it, as though it's coming from somewhere below his rib cage.

I take a deep swallow of beer. When I drink like this, the long back-breaking hours, the sleepless nights and the worry that someone is going to be killed or injured all fall away. My head fills with optimism. I am young and tough and on the edge of a new frontier, part of an elite team working its way into the ocean's secret vaults. But if I stand up and move away from the security of the table, there's a good chance I'm going to fall on my ass.

The room is blue with smoke and loud with boasts and conversation. At the next table, a barefoot young brunette in shorts and a see-through halter begins to argue with a Navy ensign. His words have a slurred bite to them. She defends herself by turning her head away. Her sun-tanned arms are planted firmly on the table. Her eyes glow, and her hair is limp with sweat. Beads of moisture run down the frosty glass that holds her drink.

Suddenly, she stands up, leans forward and cuffs the ensign on the shoulder. It is a slow-motion move that loosens her halter top and exposes everything south of her collarbones.

Noble takes a long mouthful of beer and wipes his chin. "If I were that Navy man," he says, "I'd reset my compass."

Overhearing his comment, the young woman smiles and the ensign's eyes narrow.

I turn toward Noble. "Art, how many pounds can you bench-press?"

"I'm not sure. Maybe a hundred."

"The Navy guy looks like he might be able to press three times that. He also looks like he'd be quite happy to rearrange your nose just to remember the pleasure it brings him."

Noble take a good look at the ensign's big shoulders and the school-boy grin slides off his face.

Littlehales fills our glasses with another round and looks directly at me. During the past few months, he's become a good friend, willing to listen and offer solid advice.

"You're going up to Miami to weld a new decompression chamber to the stern deck of the ship," he says. "Then you're going to run some final tests. Do you think you'll be ready to go to 400 feet by July?"

I look at him in the humid light. His questions are as sobering as a splash of cold water. "We've got problems, but I don't think they're insurmountable. The new station has thicker walls that should hold the helium. Stenuit has almost finished testing his recirculating breathing system." My words mask my deepest concern. I have no idea what will happen when the two divers and their hundreds of pieces of hardware are networked together at great depths.

We talk for a while, and then Noble gets up to leave. "Got to get back to the ship," he says, his words slurring into each other. "Promised Dan I'd spend tomorrow getting the diving locker squared away before we sail for Miami."

A few minutes later, Littlehales and his generous smile are gone, too, and I am left sitting alone, staring at the water droplets trickling down the side of my unfinished glass. Captain Tony's is empty except for two couples and the Beach Boys singing "I Get Around."

As the song finishes, I look up to see five uniformed sailors making their way to the empty table beside me.

"Do you mind if we use these chairs?" the tallest one asks.

"Help yourself."

As he leans forward to pick up the chair I recognize the trim black mustache running across his upper lip. He is the machinist mate in the submarine supply ship where the stainless steel tubes for our new carbon dioxide scrubbers were made. He asks me to join them. His name is Curtis, he's from West Virginia and he's been with the U.S. Navy for eight years. He's had a tour of duty in the Pacific and the Mediterranean. Navy life isn't easy, he tells me, but a hell of a lot better than hard-rock farming in a remote Virginia valley.

I ask Curtis to describe the most dangerous job in the Navy. He takes a long drink from his glass. Carrier pilots believe they take the most risks because they have to land their jets on a heaving deck, he says. But nuclear submarine crews will tell you they live with lethal hazards all day every day. They also have a favorite saying: there are only two kinds of ships in the Navy, submarines and targets.

He looks across the table at his shipmates. "All five of us are in the surface fleet," he tells me, "serving on a submarine supply ship. Our work isn't very glamorous, but it sure as hell is essential. If we don't fuel and fix 'em, they can't leave the harbor."

I ask him what Navy men think of civilians. He chooses his words carefully. "Whatever his special skills, a civilian is always an outsider. He's made a different, much softer kind of professional commitment. For some military men, a civilian is just a notch below the difference between friend and foe."

As Curtis is talking, two men in dark green uniforms come in and sit down at the far end of the table. The tallest starts talking to one of the sailors. The other lights a cigarette, places his lighter on top of a pack of cigarettes on the table and blows out a thin stream of smoke.

"They're from the Underwater Demolition Team," says Curtis. "Training for operations in Vietnam. They're the ocean's stealth fighters. They carry out search-and-destroy missions and then vanish back into the sea. They think they're a John Wayne wet dream."

I glance down the table at the man smoking a cigarette. Although he's wearing sunglasses, he looks familiar. He glances up from the table, and his eyes make contact with mine as if trying to figure out why a guy in a T-shirt with *Sea Diver* on its pocket is sitting with a group of men in uniform.

Finally, it is time for me to go. I thank Curtis, make my way past the empty bar stools and step out on the sidewalk. The air has a tropical morning smell. I turn and begin to walk along Greene Street.

It isn't until I reach the next intersection that I notice the soft footsteps behind me. I wait for about a minute before I glance over my shoulder. It is the sailor in sunglasses from Captain Tony's.

Filled with the fool's confidence that comes after a night of drinking, I stop beneath a streetlight and wait for him to pass. He keeps walking until he can see me clearly and then pauses to light a cigarette. He looks me up and down. "I thought it was you," he growls. "The jerk that put the bruises on my bike."

We are standing next to a vacant lot. There is no one else on the street. Sweat begins to crawl down my back.

His fist comes out of the darkness and catches the side of my chest, spinning me sideways. As I turn, I fling my right fist in his direction. My knuckles bounce off his shoulder as if it is made of cinder block. The next thing I know we are in a crouch, circling each other in the weedy grass of the vacant lot.

Suddenly there is a sting on my cheekbone and my legs begin to weaken. I dodge the next blow, but then there is a swirl of stars, my arms fall to my side and I begin to sit down slowly on the grass with my legs bent awkwardly.

I hear the wheeze of my own breath. As I try to shake away the stars, I look up to see him take a comb from his pocket and pass it along each side of his head. He looks at me as if amazed at the power in his fists. Then he reaches down and offers his hand. I'm not sure whether to take it or not.

"Sorry," he says. "I didn't mean to hit you that hard."

As I dust myself off, I notice that my wallet has fallen out of my jeans. I kneel down and begin to look through the clumps of grass. The flattened blades are bathed in a haze. The ground beneath them is spinning.

Then he is there beside me, on his knees, pushing back the grass with his hands. "Is this what you're looking for?" he asks.

As he hands me my wallet, my draft card flutters out. He picks it up, turns it over slowly in his hand and gives it to me. I slip it back inside my wallet.

"Been called up yet?" he asks.

"Not yet," I say, struggling to find the words.

"Why not?"

"I'm working on a diving project supported by the Navy."

As we step back on the sidewalk, he asks me what I am doing in Key West. I tell him who Ed Link is and what he is trying to achieve. He listens, and then invites me to go back with him to Captain Tony's for a nightcap. We sit at the bar and spend an hour talking about the weapons and tactics he will be using in Vietnam and how his friend caught a Cong mortar round in the chest.

Late the next morning, I wake up and stagger to the mirror. My right eye is the color of an overripe plum.

SEVEN

JUNE 1964. It is after midnight and I am lying on my bunk on board *Sea Diver* unable to sleep. The sky is filled with soft explosions from a line of thunderstorms crossing the Gulf Stream a few miles from our anchorage.

We spent the past month in a Miami shipyard repairing *Sea Diver* and welding a new decompression chamber onto her deck. The chamber, positioned so its main entrance hatch can lock onto the submersible chamber, gives the divers additional space for their long decompression. After the chamber was hooked up, we carried out a series of simulated dives to 400 feet to make sure its communication and life-support systems were working. Then we steamed across the Gulf Stream to Great Stirrup Cay in the northwestern Bahamas. Two days ago, for our final test, we lowered the station 70 feet to a sandy plateau surrounded by a rim of high coral. It is still down there, alone in the watery darkness.

The Bahamas are an archipelago of more than 700 islands forming a barrier between the Gulf of Mexico and the Atlantic Ocean. Rising no more than a hundred feet above sea level and exposed to the fury of seasonal hurricanes, the islands are the sun-baked tips of a 900-mile-long submarine escarpment. Bounded by huge sand plateaus and miles of coral reefs, their waters teem with amberjack, crawfish, sailfish and sharks.

I get up and look out the open porthole. Across the black, wind-blown water I see the anchor lights of two other ships. The bigger one is the Navy support ship USS *Nahant*. The other is *Undersea Hunter*. Beyond them lies the Caribbean Sea.

The Caribbean. I love the sound of its name and its warm blue waters, which have borne Spanish galleons freighted with silver and gold. I stand there and inhale the smell of warm salt water and maritime history. Then I lie down and try to sleep.

Less than an hour later, the door opens and a voice drills into my ear. "Put your feet on the floor, Doc, we need a hand topside." Lightning flares just outside the porthole. I slide into my jeans and deck shoes and climb up a companionway.

Outside, the sea is now black and covered with roaring foam. The ship is rolling heavily; every few seconds, a blinding light flashes overhead.

On the starboard side of the deck, three bare-armed men are hunched down next to a large coil of rope and hose. I release my hold on the cabin rail, stagger across the slanting deck and slide to my knees beside them. With a deep tearing sound, a black wave breaks against the hull, sending water over our shoulders.

The thunder is deafening. In the wildly intermittent light, I follow the movement of arms and hands, trying to comprehend what they are working on.

The bundled rope and hose coming off the coil has jammed itself under a cleat. Its far end, under extreme tension, leads over the gunwale and into the water. *Sea Diver* is being blown back on her anchors, and we are dragging the undersea station across the seafloor. If we haul it into a head of coral, it's going to look like a train wreck.

I begin to pull on the hose and rope, trying to gather in enough slack to unwind it from the cleat. The person on his knees beside me reaches out and places his hand on my arm. "Wait! Not yet," he shouts.

I turn my head and lean in closer to see who it is. The sky lights up the face of Ed Link breathing heavily, staring past me as if trying to gauge the rhythm of the oncoming wind and waves. A few seconds later the whole ocean rises into one toppling breaker, shakes itself into spray and falls back on itself. "Now!" he yells.

Two pairs of arms appear beside mine. We haul together, but can't get enough hose. On our second try, a sheet of lightning jumps out of the water in front of us. We release the hose and cover our ears at what sounds like a mineshaft collapsing on our heads. The air smells faintly of ozone.

On our fourth attempt, after a breaking wall of water leaves us gasping for air, we recover enough slack to clear the cleat. As the hose and rope fly off the top of the coil, someone wraps his arms around my chest and lifts me off the deck. I look down to see the loop of rope that was closing around my ankle spiral into the water. As we watch *Sea Diver* swing on her anchor and turn into the wind, I break into a shivering sweat.

Once inside, we stand shoulder to shoulder in the warmth of the galley. Our clothes look like they are running off our bodies. Link's son, Clay, plants his feet wide apart, puts his hands on the table, and shakes himself. The spray coming from his clothes encloses him in a halo of vapor.

His father's wet clothes make it easy to see a compact body shaped by years of hard work. Tonight he radiates the energy of a much younger man. After he dries himself off, Ed turns to his son. "At first light, I'd like you to pick a partner and go down to see what kind of shape the station's in."

Clay smiles at his father. "First thing in the morning, Dad, first thing."

I am hoping Clay will ask me to go with him. Since he joined the ship we have become friends, talking about our passion for the sea and the things we might do after the deep dive. For Clay, every dive is an exciting event tempered by cautious discipline. It centers him, he says, just like a gyroscope.

I once asked him what it was like to dive with his father.

"My dad pushes through the water," he said with a grin, "but I swim with cougar-like grace."

"He's getting old," I said.

"Not too old to take an occasional bite out of me."

I had seen how tough the father could be on his son, pushing him harder than the rest of the crew.

"It's his way of preparing you to take over his work when he's ready to retire."

"Being his son is tough work."

"Being anyone's son is tough work, but you've got a father who's giving you a chance to stake a claim in a whole new world."

After drying off, I go below, lie on my bunk and listen to the rain drumming on the deck. I can't get my mind away from the loop of rope that almost became a death-grip around my ankle. All my life I've felt that chaos is close at hand, not seeking me out but always ready to make an unexpected appearance.

The next morning Clay asks me to join him. We put on our masks, fins and air tanks, drop into the water and glide down into the upper reaches of the ocean. As we pass through the indigo light at 30 feet, we look down and see the trail left in the sand by the station during its trek across the seafloor. Remarkably, the fat rubber sausage is still upright and intact.

We swim down for a closer look. The black curved walls, lifting harness and high-pressure cylinders are unmarked. So is the access well and the interior. It's only when we inspect the ballast tray at the bottom of the station that we see how lucky we were. The tray holds six tons of lead shot. The hose, rope and communications wire that connect it to the ship are tied off to a metal flange at one end. Every pull from *Sea Diver* lifted the tray a few inches before jerking it forward. This kept the station from digging into the sand and tipping over.

We swim backward, plant our swim fins lightly on the sand, and take a good look around. We are swimming inside a cathedral of ancient water charged with minerals dissolved from the continents. Around us are countless animals and plants living among intermeshing layers that pass through and around each other. This is the ocean I imagined as a young boy, filled with mystery and promise. Looking up, I see the silver train of my exhaust bubbles, like pearls on a necklace, rising upward to disappear in the sunlight.

A large barracuda, shaped like a silver torpedo, circles us slowly, its white teeth gleaming the water. It turns until its body is pointed toward us. A muscular ripple runs down its back and then it springs forward. In a long, drawn-out instant, it splits the water between us and vanishes into the cyanic gloom.

We turn and follow the path the big fish has taken, swimming down an incline until we reach a hundred feet. As I swim, I try to forget everything and think only about the ocean. We are swimming in a luminous light that passes through sheer walls of blue and purple merging with one another. I follow Clay's fins over a coral ridge and across a sand flat that contains clumps of green algae and a pair of feeding stingrays. We are the first humans to see this stretch of Bahamian seafloor. Ahead lies a precipitous incline leading down into incomprehensible darkness.

Looking into the emptiness I wonder if a few places are best left alone, unexplored and untouched, forever.

We make our way back up the slope past the station, ascending through the trill of our exhaust bubbles and a halo of watery sunlight surrounding the ship. In the shimmering heat on the surface I drop my mouthpiece and inhale deeply. The ocean has a smell rich in salt and other minerals, saturated with unseen life.

❖

On June 30, at 9:30 in the morning, I stand at the railing of *Sea Diver* and watch Robert Stenuit and Jon Lindbergh slide into the ocean and swim down into the submersible decompression chamber suspended just below the surface. The sun fills the sky like a radiant pinwheel and the ocean gleams like green glass. I walk over to the dive control console on deck and listen on the intercom as Stenuit tells us they have secured both inner and outer hatches.

Slowly we increase the chamber's internal pressure until it equals 150 feet of seawater. Then we begin to winch it down to 432 feet, the depth of the station. After about an hour, Stenuit and Lindbergh reach the bottom. Through the long gas hose that connects their chamber to the control console, we increase the pressure inside the chamber until it equals the pressure of the water outside. I imagine them inflating their diving suits, opening both hatches, dropping into the cool water and swimming across to the station. Even in the twilight gloom, they can see more than a hundred feet. Moving slowly to

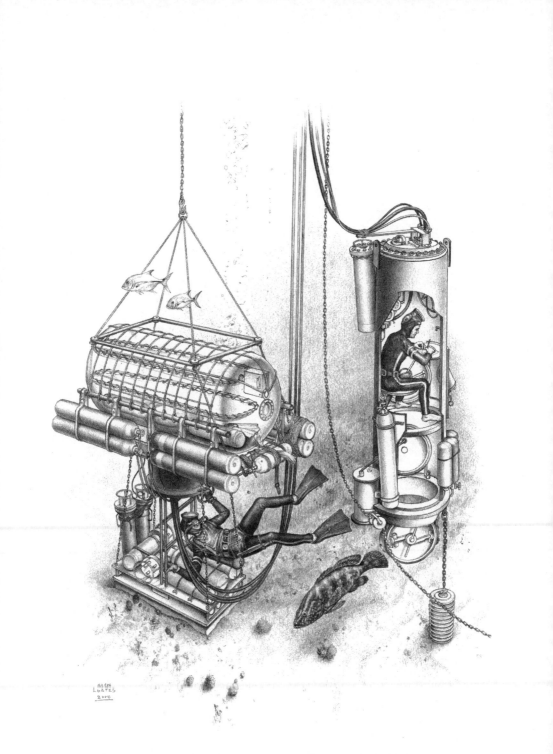

Jon Lindbergh and Robert Stenuit at 432 feet with their submersible
decompression chamber next to their undersea dwelling. *(Courtesy of Glen Loates)*

conserve energy, they climb up through the access well and begin to settle into their home under the sea.

⋯⋄⋯

A day and a half later, I turn the page of the dive logbook and make an entry. "July 2, 1964, 4:00 A.M. The wind is out of the west at less than five knots. Seas calm. Stenuit is asleep in the upper bunk. Lindbergh is awake, sitting on the lower bunk, keeping an eye on the life-support systems. After spending 38 hours at this depth, both men appear to be in good physical condition."

As I write, I keep glancing at the ghostly closed-circuit television image of Jon Lindbergh. He has wrapped a white beach towel around his head to keep warm. I suspect he is shivering, but I can't be sure. The temperature of his oxygen-helium atmosphere is cold enough for meat storage.

Lindbergh has just recently joined our team. Black-haired and slim, he came on board hesitantly, walking across *Sea Diver*'s deck with his legs slightly bent and his toes pointed out, the kind of walk that keeps a man balanced in high seas. His quick smile made us like him instantly.

Lindbergh was born in 1932, five years after the solo flight across the Atlantic that made his father, Charles, the most admired man on earth. His shyness suggests that he has inherited his mother's aversion to fame. Lindbergh has a degree in marine biology and spent several years working as a commercial diver in California. Soon after he arrived, it became apparent that his experience diving on offshore oil platforms taught him how to solve complex technical problems with minimum effort.

Lindbergh shifts position and tightens the towel around his head. It is an enormous asset having someone on the team with such quiet courage. However, if he gets injured or comes down with something as simple as a nosebleed, his celebrity name will generate two-inch headlines around the world.

It is the second night of the deep dive and I am sitting at the control console located next to the decompression chamber. The console holds pressure gauges, flow meters, the oxygen and carbon dioxide analyzers we tested at the University of Pennsylvania, a voice communication system and the video monitor. It is flanked by bundles of black hoses and wires and a dozen high-pressure oxygen and helium cylinders. Overhead, a flat canvas roof on a steel-pipe frame protects it from sun and rain. Steps away are the ship's gunwales and an unobstructed view of the black velvet sea.

Every 15 minutes I check the status of the most critical life-support indicators and enter them in the dive log. Oxygen 4 percent; carbon dioxide 0.25 percent; pressure steady at 432 feet.

The reliable accuracy of these numbers is why we spent so much time calibrating the analyzers at the University of Pennsylvania. Too much oxygen changes the function of the brain and nervous system and causes muscular twitching and convulsions. Too little means loss of consciousness, even death.

The partial pressure of oxygen in the air at sea level is 21 percent. However, at 432 feet, this percentage would be lethal. As a result, the proportion of oxygen in the breathing mixture is reduced and must be precisely controlled.

With every breath, Lindbergh and Stenuit exhale carbon dioxide, an invisible gas that accumulates rapidly in small spaces, causing headaches, dizziness, "air hunger" and eventually convulsions and unconsciousness. To control the quality of their breathing gas, a small fan blows it through a steel canister of Baralyme, a chemical that absorbs carbon dioxide.

As precise as they are, the gas percentages tell us nothing about what is going on inside the bodies of two men at the greatest ocean pressure ever endured for so long a time.

Both seem to be apparently unaffected by the massive force of the sea above them and the severe cold and lack of sleep. However, they are introspective men, so focused on the success of the mission that they are reluctant to say anything is wrong until the last possible moment.

An objective assessment of their health is hopeless. We can only see them on a small, two-dimensional video screen. In addition, the oxygen-helium they are breathing has rendered their voices into a Mickey Mouse squeak. For this reason, their vocabulary has been compressed to a few monosyllabic words that include an assortment of expletives.

Yesterday, Stenuit and Lindbergh began taking turns exploring the seafloor around the station. They struggled into their diving suits and emerged from their sunken home, swimming slowly, straining to breathe through long hoses. All of their tissues and internal organs are saturated with helium, so they knew that if they surfaced too rapidly, their cells and tissues would explode. Only a gradual decompression, lasting about four days, will bring them back safely to the surface.

They discovered that the seafloor sloping down from the station is filled with sponges and small fish. Not far from where they were swimming, the water falls more than a thousand feet into a world of black ledges, alcoves, grottos and half-domed amphitheaters. Their breathing system, with its 50 feet of closed-circuit hose, works with sluggish perfection. According to Stenuit, a curious 200-pound grouper hovers outside the station and follows them around like a shadow.

I picture the large spotted creature swimming out of the blackness, drawn by the strange light and low-frequency sounds. She sees a small, black structure recently arrived on the ledge where she searches for food. She sees two swimming forms that move slowly and appear non-threatening. She is bigger than they are and moves in closer for a better look. Her eyes are wide and unblinking. It is easy for her to follow the forms. They swim; she glides.

Early in the afternoon, when Lindbergh and Stenuit are inside the station, we conduct an experiment to determine how much air is needed to make their voices intelligible. Lindbergh inhales three times from a cylinder filled with 25 percent helium and 75 percent air and then speaks. His voice is a squeaky falsetto, but we understand him clearly. He asks us to send a telegram to his young children in California.

We are in a small rubber house on the bottom of the ocean. Hundreds of fish are swimming outside the window.... Two little octopuses were playing on the bottom under us yesterday. They would glide into a hole and then jump out at the fish. The fish darted away, but always came back to watch the octopuses. Then we swam out and they all ran away.

I look out into the blackness above the sea. A rainsquall has erased the flashing beacon from the lighthouse on Great Stirrup Cay, a reminder of the time when there were no lighthouses or charts to guide sailors through these reef-filled waters. The only thing the early mariners had going for them was their nautical skill and a large measure of luck.

We are blessed with more than our share of good fortune. For days the wind and seas have been tranquil. Our interdependent technologies—gas analyzers and breathing equipment, communication systems and the four-point moor that keeps us directly over the station—are functioning well. Best of all, we are working with two men who have the psychological resources to adapt to the outer edge of the known world.

As I turn back to study the monitor, a man in a dark blue T-shirt eases out of the night and places his hand on my shoulder. It is Ed Link. "How are they doing, son?" he asks quietly.

I look into his sleepless, bloodshot eyes. "Fine, so far so good."

Link spends a full minute staring at the pale image of Jon Lindbergh resting on his bunk and then walks over to the side of the ship. Skeins of light from the deck lamps play across his body.

The past months have taken a toll on the man. His shoulders sag and the confidence in his stride is less pronounced. There is a frown of fatigue where there was once a smile of assurance. In his own way, Link is carrying every one of us on the ship. If we succeed in establishing this encampment on the continental shelf, the laurels will be shared among us. If we fail, he alone will be held accountable. Our leader is living inside the burden of his dream.

In the weeks prior to the dive, Link talked about some of the directions his dream might take us. Several major oil and chemical companies are taking a hard look at the project because they want access to the mineral and hydrocarbon resources buried under the seafloor. If we achieve our objectives, they will try to find a way to support this kind of work in the future. Some of them are even thinking of converting our research into a commercial enterprise.

There is something about this project that has overtones of the California Gold Rush. There is the feeling that anything is possible and nothing is forbidden. On the continental shelves, a submerged territory the size of Africa, there are fortunes for the taking, vast wealth waiting for men with the right ambition and adaptability. Unfortunately, this kind of thinking brushes up against a dark side of American culture. Get in. Get rich. Get out.

In all of this, the man standing a few feet away appears to be interested mainly in advancing the technology of living inside the ocean. He made his fortune many years ago. At this point in his life, he is the captain of a ship and no longer a captain of industry. Accumulating wealth makes some men more rapacious, but appears to have no such effect on Edwin Link.

Suddenly, Lindbergh's face and towel disappear from the screen. The only thing visible is his upper shoulder. He seems to be bent over, looking into the water of the access well.

On the screen I see the small, round porthole at the end of the station lurch to one side and return to its original position. A few seconds later, the porthole moves again. I shake my head. Is the station sliding down the slope? Did a big animal swim into it? Three days ago sailors on the USS *Nahant* caught a 15-foot tiger shark that writhed on the deck, opening and closing its jaws, before the sailors tossed it back into the ocean.

"Captain, you should see this."

In two short strides, Link is at my shoulder studying the monitor.

"Why is it moving like that?" he says, his voice rising. "What's making it move?"

We hear Lindbergh and Stenuit squawking at each other. Then we hear laughter.

Lindbergh appears on the screen, smiling and pointing down at the entry well. He keeps repeating a single word.

"Can you understand what he's saying?" Link asks.

"'Grouper,' I think he's saying 'grouper.'"

Link smiles with relief. "Maybe it's the big one that's been following them around. I'll bet it's attracted to the light from the station."

I glance down at the edge of the console. Link's palms are slick with sweat. He knows that the ocean is one of the most dangerous places on earth. He knows that when you work at this depth you live with danger forever present around you. The danger might come and go, and in some cases might not even be real, but the sense of it never vanishes.

⁘

After the divers have been at 432 feet for 49 hours, Link holds a brief meeting on the deck next to the console. Behind him, sunlight lies like a sheet of diamonds on the water. Link rubs the sleep from his eyebrows and slides his fingers through his thin, gray hair. He looks at each one of us standing in front of him and chooses his words carefully. "I don't think we have anything more to gain by staying longer, but I want your opinion."

We look at each other. There are ten of us working in shifts, including my good friend Jim Dickson from the University of Pennsylvania. We thought this might happen and have talked about it. "It makes good sense," Jim says. "Decompression is going to be stressful and we want the divers in reasonable shape for the four days it's going to take to get them back to the surface." Link nods agreement and looks at the exhausted faces that surround him. "Until now," he says, "we've been lucky. Every hour on the bottom adds to the risk of an accident. I vote to bring them up."

After, Link takes me aside. "As soon as we get them in the submersible chamber," he says, "the mission moves into its final critical phase. I'm counting on you to bring them home safely."

I swallow hard. Three days ago, in the rush to get the station down to the bottom, I neglected to install an equalization valve on a steel transfer capsule holding a spare carbon dioxide scrubber. When the divers arrived in the station and the primary scrubber failed, Stenuit reached for the spare and brought it inside. Without the equalization valve, Stenuit couldn't get the cover off. The carbon dioxide inside the station climbed into the danger zone and the divers fled to the submersible chamber. It took two hours to solve the problem. My inexcusable blunder almost halted the project. As the drama unfolded, and other people solved the problem I had created, I was so shot through with adrenaline you could smell it on me like perfume.

At 1:30 P.M., Lindbergh and Stenuit swim into the submersible chamber and secure the hatches. An hour later, we begin to winch up the chamber, keeping its internal pressure at 432 feet. At 3:15, the chamber is hoisted over the side and onto its cradle. Then its internal pressure is decreased to 400 feet to make it possible for the helium to begin escaping from their tissues.

At 4:00, the chamber is mated to the deck decompression chamber, which is also at a pressure of 400 feet. Stenuit and Lindbergh transfer to the deck chamber and we begin to decompress them at the rate of five feet per hour. With the divers safely on deck, *Sea Diver* slips out of her four-point moor and we begin steaming across the Gulf Stream for Florida.

In the middle of the 10-hour crossing, I walk to the stern of the ship and look down into the Gulf Stream, the wide blue river passing under our keel. The stream's origins are in the rotation of the earth and the Atlantic trade winds that blow across the wide ocean and push a vast bulk of water steadily westward. When it reaches the coastline, the water banks up in the Caribbean Sea and deflects northward. Between the Bahamas and the coast of Florida, the Gulf Stream is about 50 miles wide and 2,000 feet deep, and flows north at a speed of about four miles an hour.

❖

July 5, 1964, 2:30 P.M. A gentle breeze is blowing from the southeast. Seas are calm. *Sea Diver* is steaming west across the Gulf Stream toward Miami. Stenuit and Lindbergh are resting inside the decompression chamber at a depth of 60 feet. So far, their decompression has proceeded without incident. In a few minutes I will enter the air lock, pressurize to their depth, and give them their first medical exam since they went to maximum pressure.

I've studied Lindbergh and Stenuit on the television screen and have seen them through the view ports of the deck chamber. Now I will be able to observe them directly. I bend over, push my black doctor's bag in front of me and crawl through the round hatch of the air lock. Drawing my knees up tightly to my chest, I turn and secure the heavy steel hatch behind me. A small, dim glow lights the air lock. I lean toward the intercom.

"The outer hatch is secure. Ready to go."

"We'll pressurize you on the count of three," says a muted voice.

"One, two …"

A jet of humid air begins filling the lock with a roar. My skin turns hot and sticky, and my ears pop. In less than a minute I am at 60 feet, the roaring stops and the hatch leading into the deck chamber cracks open. Slowly, I crawl into the chamber. The smell of dank mildew and unwashed maleness sweeps into my nostrils.

Stenuit and Lindbergh are sitting at the far end of the lower bunk, stripped to the waist, encased in sweat. Lindbergh smiles and extends his small, square hand. His face has the faraway look produced by prolonged physical effort.

Blinking slowly in the bright sanctuary light, the two men describe some of the things they saw and felt at the bottom of the sea. The astonishing visibility. The helium-amplified cold inside the station. The implosion of a lightbulb that sprayed glass over their bunks. The security of knowing the submersible chamber with its open hatch was only a short swim away. The exhilaration of roaming for hours—making observations, taking pictures and collecting samples—on the outer edge of the continental shelf. And, at night, the big grouper attracted to the column of light in the access well.

As they talk, I notice scratches on their hands and welts on Stenuit's chest. Two days of immersion and humidity have turned their skin soft and vulnerable to infection. I will send down a topical antibiotic.

I try to look into their eyes. Both men sit without moving, staring straight ahead with an air that seems distracted. For two days, they have lived inside a secret corner of the ocean, coexisting with its dangers, darkness and promise. They have exhausted their physical and mental resources. They have seen and felt things unknown to other humans.

I will never know why they did it and, perhaps, neither will they. They were attracted to Edwin Link and his dream. They were confident that he had the courage and commitment to achieve it. Young and ambitious, and willing to test themselves to the limit, they projected their dreams upon his.

I take Lindbergh's pulse and measure his blood pressure. Both are normal. Placing my stethoscope on his rib cage I listen to his chest. His lungs are clear, the air flowing down his trachea and into the tiny air sacs of his lungs with a slow and natural rhythm. It would take so little to change this, I think, something as simple as a spoonful of water inhaled from a leaking mouthpiece. The larynx would clamp down in spasm and oxygen stop flowing to the lungs. There would be a dark struggle. Quick unconsciousness. The heart would speed up and then halt. The brain would cease to consider anything. I look into Lindbergh's eyes. They have depths to look into.

As I examine Lindbergh, Stenuit is writing in a notepad. As far as I know, he is the first human ever to write from deep inside the ocean. Among his lyrical thoughts, captured in *The Deepest Days:*

The undersea realm I have visited is extracting its price of admission. Living in the depths, I have become a creature of the depths, adapted to their pressures. Now the human environment is temporarily intolerable to me ... and so I must wait inside this life-saving prison until I have been slowly weaned from pressure....

To me, the conquest of the continental shelf is the most extraordinary adventure of which a diver might dream ... I have always found joy in dangers lucidly accepted and prudently overcome....

I knew as soon as Jon Lindbergh and I began running test dives together that I could not have asked for a better partner than this dark, smiling lad, so thoughtful and courteous. By the time we reached our test site in the Bahamas, Jon and I had become a team that is better than either of us....

One of Stenuit's best descriptions is how he and Lindbergh swam from the submersible chamber into the station for the first time and were confronted with a series of mechanical malfunctions—including my unpardonable blunder.

Seen from below, the water surface inside the entry shaft is a mirror of fluid silver. My head breaks through it. The gas of the interior tastes like fresh mountain air. I climb the ladder. At last, at last, I am here. Six months of delays, of dogged effort, but now I am here. What calm there is in this other world. What silence. What peace. I shake myself. I must act quickly.

My first task is to connect the gas analyzer to its waterproof batteries. The little black needles come alive: oxygen, 4 percent, carbon dioxide, 0.25 percent. All is well.

To avoid damage in case the interior should be flooded during its descent, all the instruments, the electrical connections, and the interior equipment have been enclosed in waterproof containers attached to the ballast tray beneath the chamber. We must get them unpacked and installed.

Jon has joined me. First he hooks up the wires that will establish contact with the surface. Afterward he connects the light. The light-bulb glows, burns five seconds, and goes out. We look at each other in consternation. Is it the light bulb or the current?

We continue to work in the light of a diver's hand lamp. A noise like a gunshot slams against our eardrums. The sealed-beam bulb has imploded, spraying the inside with thousands of sharp fragments. Happily, we still have flashlights.

I plug in the radiator. Nothing. Without heat for our atmosphere and our food, things present themselves somewhat poorly....

Standing up in the narrow access well with water up to my waist, I wrestle with a four-foot aluminum cylinder. It houses a machine that will filter the gas and remove the excess carbon dioxide. At last I get its top out of water and open the equalization valve.

This valve allows pressure inside the container, sealed at sea level, to equalize with the fourteen-times-higher pressure. When the valve is opened, gas should rush into the container with a loud *psst*. Only then can the lid be removed.

I turn the valve, but nothing happens. The container is full of water. Catastrophe! Our situation is definitely not brilliant; that apparatus is vital to us.

I glance at our analyzer and see that the carbon dioxide level has risen to 1.1 percent. Our minutes here are numbered. Quickly we fetch the spare filter. It seems to weigh a ton as I thrash around on the bottom trying to drag it behind me.

Jon hands me a line. I push and he pulls; I lift and I pivot and I maneuver. I come back to the entrance well to breathe more and more often, more and more heavily. At last the monster is in place, but I am completely out of breath. Our furious efforts have raised the level of carbon dioxide to 1.7 percent.

Now we discover that this container has no pressure-equalizing valve. The surface people have put on the wrong cover. I calculate rapidly: About four tons of pressure holds that cover on. No use trying to force it off.

Can we pry it open enough to let air in under the edge? No luck. I break a screwdriver, and Jon snaps a scissors blade. A glance at the analyzer shows 2.0 percent carbon dioxide. We are panting now, breathing too fast. The heavy pounding of my heart resounds through my whole body. I make a sign to Jon: Get out. And we return to the submersible chamber, to the sure refuge....

I consider our condition. Without an air purifier, without light, without heat, perhaps without any electricity at all, it is discouraging. I write with a grease pencil on the side of the cylinder: "In any case we will stay here 24 hours."

From the level above me, Jon signals his agreement. An entire day spent below 400 feet in the cylinder would be at least a half-way success.

We report our predicament to the surface in Morse code. Link answers efficiently, as always: "We are sending you a line. Attach it to the flooded container. We have an exchange motor. We will repair and return." ...

We wait. The surface calls us. "According to my instruments, there is now more than 2 percent carbon dioxide. You have a maximum of 15 minutes inside."

When we re-enter the place, the carbon dioxide level will climb very quickly. Above 5 percent, its toxic effects will be severe, and here no rescue is possible. Those 15 minutes will decide the success of the entire operation....

We wait. It is growing dark....

Something clangs against the side of our chamber. The new air purifier has arrived. I leap into the water, shivering, and drag it over to the station. Inside, the gas seems heavy and thick, sticky in the mouth.

I open the equalization valve. This time gas rushes into the container. The purifier is dry. Jon's face lights up with joy, but we have no time to celebrate. Six minutes have passed already. The analyzer's needle creeps into the danger zone. We take off the cover, wrestle the machine into its cradle, and plug it in. The motor purrs. The gas circulates. We have won.

❖

That evening, in the last light of the sun, we ease into the port of Miami, turn south and follow the purple shadows of the waterfront to the entrance of the Miami River. A few minutes later, riding on an incoming tide, we berth at a shipyard on the river's south shore. Some of the men who tie us up to the concrete wall are young Cubans who have fled Castro's tyranny. In the streets near the shipyard, they are building a new community called Little Havana.

The night comes on, the sky continues to glow pink in the west, and the river runs black beside us. In the distance I hear the low rumble of cars and delivery trucks and, occasionally, the wail of a police siren. I am back on shore and it feels like a place I am not quite familiar with.

I look into the river as it presses against the side of the ship. The world of water and the world of land are separate and distinct. But those brief days on the other side of the Gulf Stream have shown me that beneath the surface, down at the depths of the continental shelf, water and land are one. There is no escaping it.

When we have decompressed the chamber to a depth of 33 feet, Stenuit informs us that he feels a burning inside his right leg. I go to the view port to observe him closely. He is sitting on the lower bunk calmly rubbing his knee. Somewhere, perhaps in a ligament or a section of bone, tiny bubbles are blocking the flow of blood. His tissues and nerve endings are starving for oxygen. To treat him we will have to recompress the chamber to a depth that will dissolve the bubbles. In addition, we will increase the partial pressure of oxygen he is breathing.

At a depth of 50 feet, the pain vanishes. To minimize the risk of a recurrence we slow the rate of ascent to four feet per hour. Once again I climb into the air lock and go down to examine the divers. Both are wearing masks and breathing 100 percent oxygen—a technique used to hurry the last of the helium out of their tissues. Both men tell me they are feeling well and eager to be out on deck.

At 11 o'clock the next morning, Stenuit and Lindbergh open the hatch to a scrum of journalists, photographers and television reporters. For the next two hours, they answer questions and pose for photographs. Stenuit describes the dangers of nitrogen narcosis and how it has been avoided by breathing helium. He tells the reporters that if he and Jon had stayed in the station for two weeks or two months, the decompression process would have been the same. Lindbergh describes what they saw on the bottom. Link talks about how the whole enterprise has been a team effort, his future plans for a 600-foot dive and the day, not far off, when men and women will work for a week or more at 1,000 feet.

The next day Link takes the American flag from *Sea Diver*'s stern, folds it neatly and hands it to me. "Keep this," he says, "as a reminder of how hard these past months have been and what it took to achieve our goal."

I look at the flag and the man who gave it to me. In achieving his dream, he has shown us that any act of significance is a kind of guerrilla warfare; there is no vacation and no relief. At first, there is very little chance of victory. To be successful, you work tirelessly every day. The uncertainty, the monotony and frustrations are all combated by this daily application of effort.

For the next 24 hours, in the company of my shipmates, I am filled with relief commingled with tension. Our near-accidents and close calls are behind us. We have done something that is unique. For all of us, all life is concentrated right here, forever. We have discovered that once you have experienced the interior of a new frontier, there is no going back. Once you have lived with the sun on your shoulders and the depths beckoning you can never get away from it. The great waters flow into your blood and your thoughts, and you carry them with you for the rest of your life.

EIGHT

THREE WEEKS LATER, I pack my gear and fly to Bermuda to visit the U.S. Navy's *SeaLab 1* project.

Bermuda is a cluster of small islands in the North Atlantic about 600 miles east of Cape Hatteras. The shallow water surrounding the low-lying archipelago is occupied by deep terrace reefs, rim reefs, patch reefs and sand flats. They are the most northerly reefs in the world and lie close to the surface. Their dense, interlocking walls of coral are fearsome, even in fair weather.

After about two hours of flying, the aircraft descends and the ocean suddenly turns blue-green and tawny. Beneath us is a labyrinth of patch reefs and sand. More than 300 ships, from Spanish galleons to modern-day freighters, have met their end in Bermuda's breaking waves and coral heads, and it is easy to see why. A few minutes later, we land at the airport on St. David's Island.

Early the next morning, I drive over to the U.S. Naval Station on Somerset Island and join a small group of sailors and civilians taking a 40-foot utility boat out to the dive site. As we steam toward the open sea, a young Navy photographer introduces himself. Bernie Campoli tells me that the best part of his job is going underwater to photograph the Navy's diving operations. The tense way he leans his muscular body against the railing suggests that he'd rather be under the ocean than riding across its surface in a rolling boat.

"I don't get much time to talk to square-heads," he says, beaming.

"Square-heads?"

"Civilians."

He pauses to see if I lose my smile, but on this bright, shiny day, I am wearing a permanent grin.

"So what are you doing, going to sea with us'n?"

"Us'n?"

"The U.S. Navy."

"Get serious."

"OK, so why are you here?"

In a cluster of rapid-fire sentences, I tell him about our recent deep dive that was made with the Navy's support and the invitation to take a close-up look at *SeaLab 1*. Campoli listens quietly, his eyes on the receding shoreline.

"You and I are in the wrong business."

"What's the right business?"

"Treasure hunting."

While we were in Miami, several treasure hunters came on board *Sea Diver* seeking advice from Ed Link. They were unshaven men who spoke in whispers about their work. They spent weeks in small boats using scuba equipment to search the shallow waters of the Florida Keys for storm-wrecked Spanish galleons filled with gold and silver.

"Over there, on Somerset Island, is one of my favorite square-heads."

"This should be interesting."

"His name is Teddy Tucker," says Campoli, "and he has a sixth sense for finding shipwrecks. If I had a fraction of what he has recovered from the floor of the ocean, I could retire."

"Is he the guy I read about in *Life* magazine?"

"One and the same. Tucker has found dozens of wrecks on these reefs, including a Confederate gunrunner that sank in 1864. He's got a front yard full of stuff that museums would kill for. Tucker's biggest find was the *San Pedro* treasure. A few years ago, he reached down into the sand and found what all of us can only dream of—gold bars, silver coins and a big emerald-studded gold cross worth hundreds of thousands of dollars."

We continue chatting as the Navy boat plows slowly through the water a few feet above the sand flats and razor-edged coral. We are heading south, across the open ocean to a submerged plateau called Argus Bank. As the islands of Bermuda fall away behind us, the subject turns to the man who is responsible for *SeaLab*.

Dr. George Bond graduated in medicine from Montreal's McGill University and then went to work as a family practitioner in Bat Cave, North Carolina. In the hills and hollows of the Blue Ridge Mountains, Bond delivered the old-fashioned kind of medicine, driving his battered Jeep out to isolated people, who loved him for his humor as well as his healing. He spent ten years doing medicine, surgery and everything in between, before the Navy called him up for active service.

Bond is 6 feet 4 inches tall and, in addition to his medical degree, has a Master's degree in English literature. He is a captivating raconteur with a savage wit. Early in his Navy career, he charmed his superiors into allowing him to study the medical effects of making free ascents from disabled submarines. In one test, Bond donned a buoyant ascent life jacket and swam out of the submarine *Archerfish* in more than 300 feet of water. Exhaling furiously all the way, he and his buddy Cyril Tuckfield ascended the height of a 30-story building. No one had ever done this before, and their daring demonstration set the standard for submarine escape.

But more than medical interest drove Bond. He felt that if humans were to survive on this planet, they would have to enter the underwater world and remain there to explore, observe and harvest the wealth of the oceans. He conceived a research project that he called Genesis; as a practicing lay preacher, he saw it as an important step in attaining the dominion over the sea promised in the Book of Genesis.

By the late 1950s, Bond's work in the submarine escape tank in New London inspired him to crystallize the concept of saturation diving. The idea of exposing humans to increased pressures for sufficient time to allow the human body to become fully saturated with inert gases was first conceived in 1942. It was seen as a way to improve the health and safety of tunnel and caisson workers. Fifteen years would pass before George Bond began the laboratory studies that would transform the idea into reality.

It was a brilliant way of thinking about the human body and how it absorbs and releases breathing gases. It became the critical medical concept that allowed humans to spend days under the ocean's pressure. As Bond tells it in his memoir, *Papa Topside*—the name his men use affectionately—"since the decompression penalty for even short dives to a relatively shallow depth [is] so great ... a new concept of diving practice has to be developed ... the greatest problem is the calculation and control of the gases which can be breathed safely at great depths for virtually infinite periods of time."

Jules Verne had imagined such things in *Twenty Thousand Leagues under the Sea*. George Bond provided the insight and commitment to bring Verne's concept to life.

Working with Captains Walter Mazzone and Robert Workman, Bond and his team of Navy divers spent six years testing their theory on animals in decompression chambers. Then they carried out a series of simulated dives with Navy volunteers. By 1962, they confirmed that three men could live inside a chamber at a depth of 200 feet for 12 days and be safely decompressed.

Bond made numerous proposals to the Office of Naval Research for a sea trial of saturation diving, including the use of a nuclear submarine as a seafloor station or "habitat." When the Navy turned down his proposals, he shared his medical findings with two men he greatly admired, Ed Link and Jacques Cousteau. Now, after years of scientific struggle and bureaucratic arm-wrestling, Bond has his own station—*SeaLab I*—under the ocean ahead of us.

Campoli tells me how Papa Topside was able to get his hands on an undersea station.

"Bond and his boys are masters of the old Navy art of procurement. If you can't get something through regular channels, swipe it."

"This square-head has a lot to learn," I say with a grin. "Tell me more."

"In the Navy salvage yard at Panama City in Florida, they found a discarded minesweeping float, cut it into pieces and welded it back together. They made it into a cigar-shaped station 40 feet long and 10 feet in diameter, with two view ports cut into each side. The ends of the station were configured to hold emergency breathing gas and electrical equipment. But what's really impressive is the living space in the center. It's jammed with environmental controls, laboratory equipment, and living and sleeping quarters. The guys even have a refrigerator and a shower. Access to the sea is through two entry shafts in the bottom." The wistful sound in Campoli's voice confirms that he'd like to be down there with the four-man crew.

I stand at the railing looking south. The long, blue line of the horizon becomes a long, blue line with a black speck. Slowly, beautifully, the Texas tower above *SeaLab 1* looms out of the sea. Finally, I see the two-story structure standing on its four steel legs. Moored below it is a big Navy barge, the *YFBN-12*. Several months ago in Washington, I had asked Bond why he selected this site.

"For the same reason Ed Link chose the Bahamas," he told me. "It's got good weather, a level bottom and moderate water temperature at depth."

The barge holds trailers and vans, coils of line and hose, and large cylinders of compressed gas. There is the hum of generators running and the smell of diesel exhaust. Dozens of sailors are moving about and occasionally breaking into a trot. As we climb up the boarding ladder, an officer greets us and asks a bosun to give us a tour of the support facilities.

Half the size of a football field, the barge is securely tied a short distance away from the Argus Island tower. As we walk from one end to the other, the bosun shows us the trailers and vans that are the surface team's sleeping quarters, eating area, gas-mixing station and dive control center.

Because the project did not have the funds to build a new submersible chamber, Bond's men took an old single-lock decompression chamber, stood it on its end, and re-plumbed and re-wired it. The ugly but safe haven—usually parked a few feet away from *SeaLab* in case of an emergency—is 8 feet high and 5 feet in diameter.

We stop at the side of the barge and look down into the deep blue water. All we can see is the sun's reflection.

The four men inside *SeaLab*—Bob Barth, Lester Anderson, Robert Thompson and "Tiger" Manning—have been living at 193 feet for almost a week. The bosun tells us that it took months of shipping delays, equipment breakdowns and weather postponements and five days of bull-horn seamanship to get the 40-ton *SeaLab* securely on the bottom. Now, he says, the four Navy divers, called "aquanauts," are at home under the ocean, carrying out housekeeping chores and conducting physiological studies. When they swim outside, they test equipment, inspect the legs of the tower and observe the swarms of sea life.

Barth, who has worked with Bond since the first days of the Genesis project, describes it later, in *Sea Dwellers,* like this: "The bottom is pretty flat except for a few outcroppings of coral. With the water temperature around 80 degrees, excursions outside are a pleasure. The visibility is all you can ask for. We can see all four legs of the Texas tower. Sea life is abundant. There are large schools of amberjack and grouper and other creatures. We have all the time in the world and no one is telling us we can't do something. The sea is ours."

Over coffee, a sailor describes a recent near-fatality. One of the aquanauts, Tiger Manning, was supposed to take pictures of *Star 1,* an experimental mini-sub, mating with a simulated nuclear submarine hatch. At one point, he had to return to the station to get more film. He was in a hurry and, on his way back out of the entry hatch, unwittingly struck his gas-control yoke and shut off his oxygen supply. Five minutes later, Manning sensed something was wrong and sprinted back to the hatch. Just as he swam under its rim, he lost consciousness. As he floated up, his tank struck *SeaLab*'s hull. The metallic sound alerted the watch-stander, Lester Anderson, who went over to the hatch and saw his friend lying face down in the water. He jumped in, lifted Manning's head and called for help. They revived Manning and got him up into his bunk. The sea may be theirs, but only on the sea's terms.

❖

The bosun tells us that the aquanauts will spend four more days living inside their damp, tubular apartment, swimming outside to work. On the afternoon of July 31, they will begin their two-day decompression to the

SeaLab 1—home to four U.S. Navy divers, Barth, Manning, Thompson and Anderson, for 11 days at a depth of 193 feet. *(Courtesy of Glen Loates)*

surface. Bond's original plan was to have them remain submerged for three weeks, but a tropical hurricane is brewing in the south and no one, especially the safety-conscious Bond, wants to recover the aquanauts when the wind is blowing at 70 knots and the waves are as high as buildings three floors high.

I have been observing Bond closely all day. He seems able to watch the weather, the sea and his men simultaneously. He shuffles in and out of the command van, talking to the divers on the bottom and the sailors on the barge, praising them, informing them and scolding them, always with the same laconic humor. I have never seen a military officer so well respected.

That evening, as the sun slides into the western ocean, I finally have a chance to speak to him. He is standing just outside the command van wearing a short-sleeved Navy-issue shirt. A stopwatch hangs on a white cord around his neck. I wait until he has finished lighting his pipe.

Bond tells me how much he admires Ed Link and his engineering and business skills. "He's done a great job getting his business associates to invest in the ocean. You are fortunate to be working for him. Things happen so much faster in the corporate world."

I look at the great barrel chest that has made the world-record free ascent out of a submarine. This is a man who embodies the mood of the time—competition and conquest. It is evident in Vietnam and the global struggle against the Soviet Union. It is an integral part of the race to the moon. We are all its captives.

At first glance, George Bond and Ed Link seem quite different. Link is a shy, self-made millionaire from upstate New York. Bond is a Shakespeare-quoting physician from Appalachia. But both men have the courage to step up to the edge of a precipice and believe they can make it to the other side. No matter how crazy the idea. Like living at the bottom of the sea.

Bond asks me about our dive and I give him a short version of what took place in the Bahamas. He is genuinely interested, like a father asking about the health of one of his offspring.

"And when will you be ready to send us the technical report?"

"I think we'll have it completed in about three months."

"Is that civilian time or Navy time?" His smile is contagious.

The next afternoon, the U.S. Navy gives me permission to put on a face mask and fins and swim over to the nearest leg of the tower. As soon as I enter the water and take a few strokes, the noise of the barge drops away.

The water is deep blue and clear. I look into the depths, hoping for a glimpse of the bright orange station, but all I see are wavering shafts of falling sunlight.

About halfway between the barge and the leg of the tower, I take a deep breath and drop below the surface. Far below, two divers, secure in their technical armor, are swimming among grouper and amberjack. The leg of the tower looks like a vertical reef, festooned with gorgonians and soft coral. Barracuda swim around it in a tightly packed school.

I look up at the tower. Inside its tall wooden structure are a laboratory and living quarters for as many as 40 scientists and support staff. They spend weeks at a time studying the physical and acoustical properties of the ocean. This information is critical to the undersea conflict called "the silent war."

For almost two decades, NATO and Soviet Navies have been fighting for dominance of the ocean depths. When the contest began just after the Second World War, the main function of submarines was to track and torpedo surface ships. Now the Soviets have ballistic-missile submarines, or "boomers," that can approach American shores and unleash a dozen nuclear-tipped missiles. To counter this threat the Americans are building a fleet of nuclear attack subs. Their mission is to stalk the Soviet subs and target them before they launch their warheads.

The moment a submarine slips below the surface, it becomes invisible. Virtually all knowledge about its speed and direction has to be gleaned from sound, the only form of information-bearing energy that travels easily through water. In the 1950s, America began building seafloor listening devices to monitor the ocean with ultra-sensitive hydrophones linked to powerful computers. The first sites of this sound surveillance system, or SOSUS, were off the east coast of Canada and the

United States. Bermuda is one of 35 locations around the globe that monitors the tactical maneuvers of Soviet nuclear submarines.

I peer down through the depths. *SeaLab 1* is more than an exercise in medicine and engineering. It is the first step in using the ocean for top-secret military intelligence tasks. It's an integral part of the Navy's strategic plan.

NINE

SEPTEMBER 1964. He leans his gaunt, angular face to one side and looks at me with bright blue eyes. "Now that you've successfully completed your long deep dive," he says, "what's the best technology to guide us into the future?"

I take a deep breath. Jacques Cousteau, the world's most acclaimed undersea explorer, the man who co-invented the aqualung, wants my opinion about the machines that will carry us into tomorrow's depths. For the past hour, in this small Boston restaurant overlooking the harbor, Cousteau has been quizzing me about our dive in the Bahamas. How well did the breathing systems work? How effective is the decompression schedule? Were there any psychological problems? Next summer, he tells me, he is going to embark on his *Conshelf Three* project, in which six men, including his son Philippe, will spend a month inside an 18-foot structure at more than 300 feet. It will be the first time anyone has spent so much time at this depth.

I look into the sea-weathered face of the *grand seigneur* of diving and realize that I have no idea what he is talking about. Does he mean breathing technology or decompression technology? Does he mean something else?

Cousteau takes a small bite of lobster, leans back in his chair and smiles.

"The best technology," he says, "is an idea."

"You mean new technologies make us think in new ways?"

Cousteau's smile seems to shrink. He is having lunch with someone who can't keep up with him.

Jacques Cousteau inspired audiences around the world with his
Conshelf projects and his documentary films. *(Courtesy of Glen Loates)*

"The pioneering work being done by Edwin Link, George Bond and our group in France," he says, "is leading to a time, let's say in the mid 1970s, when men will live underwater for months drilling for oil, mining for minerals and farming seafood. But more important than the new wealth will be the flow of ideas and creativity from humans living in a new world."

He pauses and takes a drink from his glass. A couple leaving the restaurant walk past the table, recognize him and then move on. "It is a subject Dr. Bond and I have spent many hours talking about."

Later, an attractive woman in her late twenties approaches the table and asks Cousteau for his autograph. He takes out a pen and turns to look up at her face. She has long black hair and dark brown eyes. She says that his book *The Silent World* started her thinking about life in the sea and marine biology. She is now at the University of Maryland working on her post-graduate degree.

Ten years ago, the same book cast its spell on me. It was packed with information and drama and, like *Twenty Thousand Leagues under the Sea,* took me down into inaccessible depths. It had many poetic passages. I especially remember the lyrical description of Cousteau's first dive:

> I breathed sweet, effortless air. There was a faint whistle when I inhaled and a light rippling sound of bubbles when I breathed out.... A modest canyon opened below ... the sand sloped down into a clear blue infinity.... I kicked the fins languidly and traveled down, gaining speed.... I stopped kicking and the momentum carried me on a fabulous glide. I slowly emptied my lungs and held my breath. The diminished volume of my body decreased the lifting force of water and I sank dreamily down....

Two years later I joined a rapt theater audience to watch *Le monde du silence,* Cousteau's Oscar-winning documentary. There were scenes of suntanned men working on the deck of *Calypso,* Cousteau's research ship. There were divers holding phosphorous torches and swimming through

pale blue depths toward strange and colorful life forms hidden among
coral reefs. It was high adventure on the open sea.

I look across the table at the 54-year-old man in the blue jacket and
white silk turtleneck. His Frenchness trails him everywhere. It is a part of
him, from the way he walks into a room certain of a grand welcome to
the way he is talking in his low voice to the young woman.

The ocean made Cousteau. It was his luck to be in the right place
at the right age with the right intelligence and commitment. As the
years passed, he leveraged his success with the sea into a performance
of personality. There is his cultivated style: on board *Calypso,* he wears
a long-sleeved blue denim shirt and a red watch cap; on land, he dons
exquisitely tailored suits and the trademark turtleneck. Then there are
his calculated mannerisms: the graceful walk across the bridge deck of
Calypso to gaze at the horizon and the effortless entry into the sea at the
beginning of every dive. Finally, there is his elegant accent with its
lyrical cadence and long reflective pauses.

His greatest invention is himself. He understands the power that
comes from embedding his name in the public imagination and keeping
it visible. Ed Link is uncomfortable being interviewed; Cousteau plays the
media with consummate skill, carefully arranging his words in short,
poetic sentences. He understands the potency of a dramatic photograph
of a large shark or ancient shipwreck. At heart, Cousteau is a spellbinding
storyteller.

"So tell me," he says, after the young woman has left. "What are
Mr. Link's plans for the future?"

Like most of the questions he has been asking, this one has a hidden
edge. Two years ago, Ed Link tied *Sea Diver* to a pier in the harbor at
Monaco and drove up the hill to the Oceanographic Museum to meet
Cousteau and discuss the possibility of working together. After a brief
tour of some of the high-ceilinged, ornate rooms, they went into
Cousteau's white-walled office, with its big desk and magnificent views of
the Mediterranean and Côte d'Azur. Both men were working on the same
problem—living under the sea—but taking different approaches. Link
was focusing on depth; Cousteau was focusing on duration. Perhaps, if

they pooled their resources, they could save money and find a quick solution to both. After a probing discussion about who was going to do what, the room filled with uneasy silences. There was the American way and there was the French way, and there was an ocean in between. Since that day, they have been amiable but wary competitors.

"Mr. Link has said publicly that he would like to make a saturation dive at 600 feet, and then move deeper to 800 and 1,000 feet."

Cousteau leans forward and looks at me directly. "And how will he support these experiments?" he asks.

I tell him what has been recently announced in New York. "Mr. Link and some Navy colleagues, including Admiral Stephan, the former oceanographer of the U.S. Navy, are forming a commercial diving and underwater engineering company. It will be a joint venture with the Singer Corporation, General Precision and Union Carbide."

Cousteau silently assesses the implications of this information. Three big American companies with considerable financial assets. A management team that includes former high-ranking U.S. Navy officers. Link's new company will be a formidable commercial enterprise.

He takes another sip of his wine and a small forkful of food. "If you were living on a research ship for a month," he says, "what would be your choice of cuisine?" When I tell him that I prefer Italian and French cooking to the heaps of meat and potatoes that appear on American plates, he begins a discourse on the sensuality of food. Food is much more than an amalgam of nutrients to keep the body alive, he says. Food is sustenance for the soul. Tasting food is a form of knowing, a school for the senses that transports us back to the land and sea where the food comes from. "When we sit around the dinner table on board *Calypso*," he says, leaning back in his chair, "the food and wine in front of us is a form of belonging, a starting point for stories and dreams."

Four years earlier, I traveled through Europe trying to figure out what I was going to do with the rest of my life. In the south of France, in the harbor at Nice, I happened upon *Calypso* tied up alongside the pier. I couldn't help myself. I slipped on board and peered through one of the portholes. In the living and dining room, which stretched the width of the aft main deck—the biggest and busiest room in the ship—I saw a long table covered with plates of food and bottles of wine, surrounded by a dozen men, the air in the room filled with blue smoke from Gauloise cigarettes, everyone gossiping, making jokes and talking about the day's work. There were young faces projecting strength and courage, and older faces lined from long days squinting in the sun. Around that table were men who swam into an alien world and found themselves at home.

Back in the restaurant, the conversation shifts to the medical criteria for selecting extreme-depth divers. I explain how we follow the American space program and subject our candidates to an intensive examination ranging from long-bone X-rays to pulmonary and liver function tests and brain wave studies. "It's time consuming and expensive, but when the tests are complete we know just about everything about their anatomy and physiology." I drain my glass. "And how do you select your divers?" I ask, confident that I have impressed him with our exhaustive approach.

Carefully, Cousteau picks up his wine glass and places it on the white tablecloth next to mine. Then he takes the bottle of Bordeaux and fills both glasses.

"Our method is a little less formal. We spend months living and working together on board our ship. When we want to make a serious decision about someone's future, we go to dinner and share a bottle of wine. During the first hour we know if he is the right person for the challenge."

A waiter wearing a white jacket and black bow tie comes to the table, bows slightly and says, "Captain Cousteau, I am sorry to bother you, but you have a telephone call from France. If you please, follow me."

"Forgive me," says Cousteau. "It must be important." He rises, folds his napkin and walks toward the front of the restaurant. As he walks past the tables, several people look up and gaze at him.

As with all great men, it is difficult to define Cousteau's essence. Behind the wire-frame glasses and blue eyes that never seem to blink is an irresistible force of curiosity, conceit and cleverness.

Cousteau is a twentieth-century synthesizer, a man who embraces art and science and fuses them together in arresting ways. With his aqualung, he gave the world a passport into the upper layers of the ocean. With his books and films, he elevates the ocean's inner beauty to our level of consciousness. With his *Conshelf* projects, he shows us how we might safely live within its depths. It is 1964 and he is already talking publicly about *Homo aquaticus,* a new kind of human that will come into being shortly after the year 2000. These "men fish" will have their lungs filled with an incompressible fluid. They will extract oxygen from the ocean by means of artificial gills. They will be able to swim as deep as a mile and stay underwater for months.

After we finish dessert, Cousteau asks if I love the ocean. I pause, struggling for the right answer.

He smiles. "For those who really love her," he says, "the ocean confirms there is more to this planet than highways, skyscrapers and shopping malls. The ocean mocks the assumption that buying and selling is the only way to live. The ocean is a force for change."

"What change?" I ask tentatively.

"It depends on who wants to make the change," he says.

As we are leaving the restaurant, Cousteau invites me to come to France and see the work his team is doing in their research lab in Marseille. He asks me if I've read Rachel Carson's recent book. I say that I've been too busy to read anything except technical journals. "She is a remarkable visionary," he tells me. "She has written some wonderful books on the sea, and now she is very concerned about the dangerous effects of runaway chemicals, especially pesticides. There are hundreds of these chemicals and they are in our rivers and lakes and perhaps our bloodstreams. *Silent Spring* is a courageous book. You should read it."

TEN

I **LOOK AT THE FAINT LINES** the sea wind has etched at the corners of Bev Morgan's green eyes. The 30-year-old professional oil field diver from California has a calm expression on his face. For Morgan, this is just another dive.

For me, it prompts a dialogue with fear. My heart beats rapidly. My fingers feel numb. And we are still on the surface.

Morgan and I are sitting side by side on a taut canvas bunk with a steel-pipe frame. Three feet in front of us, the curved white wall of the compression chamber glistens with moisture. In a few minutes, after we have completed our pre-dive checklist, Morgan and I are going to compress to 650 feet, a depth to which only a handful of humans have gone. The palms of my hands are slick with sweat.

It is autumn 1965. Ed Link and his partners in General Precision, the Singer Corporation and Union Carbide, have purchased and merged two commercial diving companies in Santa Barbara, California, and Morgan City, Louisiana. They have won an exclusive contract with the U.S. Navy's Supervisor of Salvage. Within the space of a few months, the new company, Ocean Systems Inc., with headquarters in New York and Washington, has become the biggest diving and underwater engineering company in the world.

The nearest ocean is hundreds of miles away. Our diving research facility is located in a suburb of Buffalo, New York, in part of a sprawling complex of laboratories and manufacturing facilities operated by the Linde Division of Union Carbide. Linde makes industrial gases such as acetylene, nitrogen and oxygen.

As the medical director of the new company, I am responsible for the health and safety of more than 50 commercial and research divers. One of my first assignments was to spend time in California and Louisiana getting to know the men who worked in the offshore oil fields of the Santa Barbara Channel and the Gulf of Mexico. I did a full medical exam on each one, and watched them step over the side of drilling rigs and supply ships and dive down to repair oil wellheads and gas pipelines.

Most of them are in their late twenties and early thirties, lean, muscular men who don't say much but possess a wide range of mechanical and electrical skills. There is nothing on a boat or barge they can't tear down and fix.

Fortunately for a physician curious about their behavior and motivation, they have an affinity for alcohol. The most informative time I spent with them was in the neon-lit bars of Santa Barbara and Morgan City.

Amid wafting cigarette smoke and wailing music, we talked about girlfriends, ex-wives, their former work as abalone divers and the new underwater technology that allows them to work in the oil fields. Sometimes we talked about the war in Vietnam and the draft dodgers who went to Canada.

Occasionally, I asked them what they thought of the risks they were taking. Most of them just stared at me and said nothing. They were in the front line of commercial oxygen-helium diving and were getting paid a lot of money. They knew all about ruptured lungs, nitrogen narcosis, aseptic bone necrosis and a host of other debilitating traumas, but disguised their fear with hard drinking, breezy humor and colorful stories of accidents that happened to someone else—the lacerated arm, the two-day concussion and the blowup from 150 feet. It helped explain the drunken binges that begin almost as soon as they come ashore and that last for two or more days.

I look at Morgan sitting on the bunk in his fire-resistant coveralls, reading the checklist over the intercom to our surface support team. Above his right shoulder, a carbon-dioxide scrubber hums next to the gleaming valves and gauges of a life-support panel. A small bench next to our knees holds the hoses and mouthpiece of a device to measure our pulmonary function. We are enmeshed in an ironclad web of technology. I breathe in slowly. The chamber smells like a drainpipe.

Bev Morgan, with his solid, muscled build, has spent years climbing over the sides of ships in heavy diving gear. His experience in the offshore oil fields makes him an ideal candidate for our land-based research program.

The dive we are about to make will simulate the pressure found at 100 fathoms under the ocean. It will tell us much about human physiology during a rapid compression and prepare us for an upcoming saturation dive at this depth. It will also verify that we have made the right mathematical choices for our recently developed decompression schedules.

I have volunteered for this dive because I want first-hand experience of working at great depths. I also want the respect of men such as Bev Morgan. Unlike Morgan, I don't make a living in an environment that is cold, dark and dangerous with an atmosphere 800 times as dense as air. I am a doctor who earns his keep dispensing cautious advice about diving medicine. Despite what they say to me, I know the company's commercial divers are suspicious of anyone who can't splice a wire rope or bench-press a 200-pound anchor. This dive will help offset their distrust of a man who spends a lot of time reading and writing.

There is another reason. We are in the midst of a series of first-ever experimental dives and have asked our commercial divers to participate. We have to show them our willingness to share the risks.

I look around the interior of the stark white chamber and try to suppress my prickly dread. At maximum pressure, there will be more than 300 pounds per square inch on the walls. What happens if a through-hull fitting begins to leak? What if one of the view ports blows out? I imagine the thunderous explosion as everything inside the chamber, including my soft, pink body, streams through a six-inch opening.

An arm reaches inside, finds the locking handle on the hatch and pulls it shut. There is a dull clunk and the chamber falls silent. A half turn of the handle seals the hatch against its circular steel rim.

Morgan shifts in his seat beside me. He looks down at his hands and then at the white fireproof paint covering the curving steel wall. "Let's get this thing moving," he mutters.

For Morgan, a dive in the open ocean is a routine descent, feet first, over the side of a work barge wearing a heavy metal helmet and a thick canvas suit, a swift fall at the end of a hose into blue-green waters with the sun dimming above. On this dive, there is no water and no toolbox, but Morgan is the kind of man who has told himself that he will never be intimidated by the ocean, no matter what it has in store for him, and he will excel at his job, no matter what form it comes in.

"If you're ready, we'll start the countdown." The voice on the inter-com is faint, authoritative. Outside the chamber, a cluster of white-coated physiologists and technicians peer at us through the view ports, poised to begin the experiment. Three weeks of planning and a half day of check-lists, and the final preparations are over.

"OK, topside, we're ready. Let's take her down," I say, hoping no one hears my sticky-lipped enunciation.

"Five, four, three … two … one."

A hard hissing sound, like a brush fire in the treetops, roars out of a gas pipe in front of my face. Waves of dry helium flame across my skin. As I inhale, hot eddies slam into my lungs. As the noise and the pressure increase, I feel a searing pain in my eardrums. I hold my nostrils and blow, trying to force enough gas into my middle ear to balance the rapidly increasing pressure.

I will always be a newcomer to the ancient business of diving. It is a profession that involves almost daily confrontation with three of the four elements—water, air and earth. Now, Morgan and I are inside the fourth, a fire without flames, a scorching heat that leaves pinpricks of pain on my lips and eyebrows.

"Three hundred … four hundred." The voice on the intercom is barely audible.

Morgan and I lean over, bending our heads against the blast. I try to focus on the holes in the stainless steel grating on the floor of the chamber. Sweat rolls down my chest and arms. The only movement is the slim black needle climbing the white numerical face of the main pressure gauge. We are descending at 100 feet a minute; every 60 seconds 50 pounds of pressure is added to every square inch of our bodies.

I try to imagine the trillions of oxygen-helium molecules rushing into my lungs and bloodstream. Propelled by my pounding heart, the molecules are storming into the hundreds of tissues and organs that give my body its form and function. I can only guess at the effect they are having on the complex strings of protein inside my brain cells. Helium, I am told, is inert. If so, why does my body feel like wax?

"Six hundred."

The roar is diminishing, but heat is still boiling out of the gun-barrel pipe in front of us. Morgan's full, unlined face and the shadow at the base of his throat are streaked with sweat. His T-shirt is clinging to his chest. He stares at me, blinking slowly.

"Six hundred and fifty feet. You are on the bottom."

The chamber falls strangely quiet. I feel light-headed and dizzy. My temples pulse. In front of me are wavering lines that look like the heat shimmer over a summer highway.

Morgan holds his hands in front of him. The skin of his palms is rough and cracked. He spreads his fingers and they begin to flutter. I place my open fingers next to his. It looks like we both have an advanced case of Parkinson's disease.

"Weeeoow. Theeshoo." The high-pitched helium sounds fall from Morgan's lips, echo briefly on the walls of the chamber, and disappear into the curving brightness. He grins at the squeakiness of his voice.

Reaching up to adjust the oxygen flow meter, I feel a twinge of discomfort in my left shoulder. I shrug my shoulders and flex my wrists. My joints feel as though they have been drained of every drop of lubricant.

Moving with the deliberation of a bomb disposal expert, Morgan flips a pair of toggle switches, turns a valve and places a small black mouthpiece between his teeth. The mouthpiece is attached to a plastic tube that goes into one end of a brushed aluminum box braided with wires. The pressure-compensated device is designed to measure the rate and depth of our helium respirations.

A face looks at us through one of the chamber's view ports. Dr. Bill Hamilton, a pulmonary physiologist and Air Force reserve pilot, is the director of our physiological testing program. "Begin breathing," he says, "as fast and as deep as you can."

Morgan takes a deep breath and starts into his deep-sea work, his eyes partially closed, inhaling and exhaling, pumping his lungs and the bellows inside the box, his efforts sending pulmonary data along slender wires through special fittings to a recorder outside the chamber. I picture Hamilton at a console studying five black pens making erratic lines on a rolling strip of paper. Working alongside him is a small group of men surrounded by banks of instruments, cylinders of high-pressure gases, and tables covered with notebooks and coffee cups.

Two minutes later, Morgan's face is strawberry red from the energy he is putting into his work. For Morgan, diving is not only a way of life—it *is* life, something he needs to meet head on. Diving seems to satisfy a need to test himself against the ocean while he is still young and at the peak of his physical health.

It is my turn. I clip on a fresh mouthpiece, place it between my lips, wait for instructions and begin blowing. The gas is so dense I feel like I am like breathing through sand. An entire minute passes followed by another.

"Breathe deeper. Keep your eye on the flow loop."

I'm not listening. My eyes are closed, my head and upper body moving up and down with the effort. When at last I take out the mouthpiece, the chamber is spinning and Morgan is smiling at me.

It takes a full minute to slow the chamber's rotation and catch my breath, long enough to wonder if this kind of activity might put too severe a strain on the human body, especially mine. I've talked to old-timers who still believe that the only honest way to get to the bottom of the sea is by wearing a thick canvas suit, lead boots and breathing fresh air inside a bronze diving helmet. For them, breathing high-pressure helium is a dangerous option.

A minute passes. A short time ago, the helium felt like hot cement on my skin. Now it has cooled to a reasonable temperature. As my breathing returns to normal I feel a surge of well-being, as though, somehow, I've taken control of my new environment.

Our second task is to lift a stack of 50-pound weights from one side of the chamber to another. It is designed to simulate the muscular effort of an oil field diver working on a wellhead. Feeling vaguely euphoric, I attack it vigorously. Pick up. Swing. Lower. Pick up. Swing. Lower. The sweat begins to trickle off my forehead and drip to the floor. At the end of 10 minutes of this, all feelings—anxiety, thirst, even the pain in my shoulders—become indistinguishable from exhaustion.

Morgan's biceps are as thick as a bridge cable. He regards the weights with level blue eyes and begins moving them with rhythmic discipline. He toils for 10 minutes without breaking a sweat. After he places the last weight on the floor, he uncurls his hands and holds them up for inspection. The trembling has diminished. From uncounted hours working in the depths of the Santa Barbara Channel, every fingernail is worn short.

From the beginning, Morgan and I try to break helium's stranglehold on our vocal cords. We speak slowly, in simple phrases, but at this pressure the sounds coming out of our throats are almost impossible to understand. In addition, something in the helium has begun to affect my temperature-regulating center. Within seconds I sweat, shiver and then sweat again. The pores of my skin seem to open and close like shutters.

Forty minutes after it starts, our consignment to 100 fathoms is over. We climb into thick sweat suits, sit on the edge of the lower bunk and wait.

"Three, two, one," says an airy voice. Suddenly, the chamber fills with the sound of a distant waterfall. Through a small, round opening over our heads, helium and oxygen molecules are flowing into the outside world.

"Six hundred and thirty."

"Six hundred and ten."

"Six hundred."

Morgan and I sit side by side as the chamber empties and cools, staring at the thin wisps of condensation forming in front of us. The chill vapors tickle my throat. I inhale and exhale very carefully, aware that if I hold my breath, the expanding gas could tear apart my lung tissue, invade my brain, block my blood flow, and leave me paralyzed or dead.

"Five hundred and fifty."

"Five hundred."

As the temperature plummets, Morgan and I shiver violently. For warmth we fold our arms across our chests, lean forward and watch the needle on the depth gauge make a steep climb back up through the depths.

"Four hundred and eighty."

"Four hundred and forty."

I look up at the small, round opening where the gas is rushing out of the chamber. If I put my hand too close to it, my skin would be removed with surgical swiftness.

"Four hundred and twenty."

"Four hundred."

"Three hundred and seventy. This is your first stop. You've arrived at your first stop. How're you feeling?"

"Damn cold, thank you," says Morgan. His voice has lost some of its helium shrillness.

Our first ascent toward the surface was a substantial one. In less than four minutes we covered 280 feet. From this point on, our decompression will be more complex and time-consuming. Because of the helium circulating inside our bodies, we have to follow a precision schedule, depth and breathing gases that will take 20 hours.

Morgan and I stand up in a half crouch, stretch our arms as best we can and then lie down in our bunks. In a few hours, dinner will be passed through a small air lock. Both its hatches will be closed and air will be let into it. When the pressure equals that inside the chamber, it will be safe to open the inner hatch.

I pick up a book, but can't concentrate. I lie back and try to picture our teammates working outside the thick steel walls of the chamber. Dr. Heinz Schreiner is a molecular biologist and expert in the design of decompression schedules. Pat Kelly is a young computer programmer. For the past eight months, both have been feeding streams of mathematical and physiological data into an IBM 360 computer to devise what we think are the most advanced decompression schedules in the world. We hope this dive and the others that follow will verify their work. I look across the chamber at Morgan. He is reading a technical manual about diving helmets and smiling to himself. Having spent hundreds of hours under the ocean's weight, he knows our lives are in the confident hands of other men.

Hours pass. We eat dinner and listen to country-and-western music piped in over the intercom. Afterward, we talk about the beginnings of commercial diving in California. In a voice that is becoming increasingly easy to understand, Morgan tells me how he became part of an underwater work force that has almost a hundred years of history.

The first commodity to lure canvas-suited divers into the cold, clear waters off the California coast was abalone, a delicious shellfish that grew in abounding numbers along the rocky shoreline. After the California Gold Rush, Chinese immigrants who had been brought over to work the mines began harvesting cartloads of red, pink, green, white and black abalone from the coves and bays south of San Francisco. As the abalone disappeared from the tidal flats, divers began wading out to recover them from the nearshore kelp beds.

By the early 1950s, most of the abalone had been strip-mined from shallow waters, and divers were moving into increasingly deeper depths and staying for longer periods of time. Men would spend five or six hours searching the seafloor for the oval-shaped shellfish. Before they could surface they had to spend an hour or more decompressing, hanging on to a rope beneath their boat, shivering, looking out for sharks.

In the mid 1950s, offshore oil companies, with their work barges, drilling platforms, supply boats and underwater pipelines, invaded the Pacific Ocean off Santa Barbara. Abalone divers took one look at the comfortable shipboard living quarters and decided that diving beneath an oil rig to service its machinery was far more profitable than hunting for elusive shellfish.

In 1956, the first diving company dedicated exclusively to offshore oil was formed in Santa Barbara. At that time, Morgan was still diving for abalone off Newport Beach.

"I remember leasing my first abalone boat," he tells me. "*Jeanne Marie* was 19 feet long and powered by a small outboard motor. I used to take her out to San Clemente Island, 50 miles from Newport Beach, where the abs were as big as dinner plates and as thick as river stones. I dove alone. On a good day, when the seas were calm, I'd spend five or six hours at 60 feet and bag hundreds of abalone. Every two days a pickup boat would drop fresh supplies and offload my catch. I'd stay out there, in good weather and bad, for as long as 20 days. At night I'd sleep under a canvas awning rigged up in the stern. My sleeping berth was a pipe frame about the size of the one we're sitting on. It was damn hard work. And lonely."

And dangerous. I could picture Morgan alone in the water at 60 feet, his head inside a bronze helmet, prying rows of pink abalone off submarine ledges as a surface wind tugged on his boat and anchor. I could see him at the end of the day in the twilight, decompressing under his boat, shivering with cold, unable to go to the surface, as a great white shark glided in and out of the shadows.

As the hours pass, I discover that Morgan is a brilliant innovator, one of those men with the talent to convert personal hazards into safety equipment. Because he hates being cold, he tailored a new closed-foam material into one of the first wet suits for commercial divers. To reduce the amount of air he was consuming, he designed a lightweight helmet with a breath-by-breath regulated breathing system.

More hours pass. We turn down the lights inside the chamber and try unsuccessfully to sleep. At eight in the morning, scrambled eggs and coffee are delivered through the air lock.

I first notice the pain at 50 feet. It arrives like a phantom, touching the inside of my right knee and then disappearing. I move my leg. Everything feels fine.

A few minutes later I feel it again, a light gnawing sensation below my right kneecap. I rub my knee and straighten my leg. The discomfort disappears.

I look over at Morgan. He is sleeping on his back with a book open on his chest. I start to read a magazine stowed under my bunk. Its airbrushed photographs fail to divert me.

The pain returns, increases and then vanishes. Is it real or imagined? If it is real, I don't want to wait too long to ask for help. If microscopic bubbles are beginning to block the blood supply to my knee, then oxygen is no longer reaching some of the cells in my bones. The flicker of fire in my nerve endings might be a warning. If I don't stop the ascent and get recompressed to a deeper depth, the cells might die. I could end up with a painful disability and a permanent limp.

If the ache is imagined, I will unnecessarily derail a decompression schedule that all of us are working hard to perfect. We are now at 43 feet. I decide that if the pain becomes more intense during the next scheduled drop in pressure I'll report it to the surface team.

A soft hiss issues from the exhaust pipe. Morgan shifts position in his bunk. I look around the chamber, savoring its history. It is the one we used to decompress Stenuit and Lindbergh in the Bahamas, modified to serve as a research chamber.

The pain is severe now and in both knees. As I reach out to press the intercom switch, my fingers are trembling.

"Topside, we've got a problem. It feels like I've been hit in both knees."

"You sure, Doc? We're almost home."

I am sure. Red-hot coals are burning in both knee joints. I swing my legs off the bunk and try to stand up. My legs buckle.

"Damn," I say.

A face fills the view port. Morgan turns on his side and looks at me suspiciously.

"I think we'd better turn around," I say, "and go back down. Both my knees are on fire."

A murmur of voices comes out of the intercom. A consensus is quickly reached. "Okay, Doc. Stand by. We're going to increase the pressure at 10 feet a minute."

My ears sense a gentle pulse of pressure. In three minutes, we travel back down more than 30 feet, a distance it took hours to cover on the way up.

We stop at 80 feet. Morgan is sitting up, looking at me. "Are you okay?" he asks. "You look a little pale."

I am breathing quickly and my heart is drumming. The pain is not going away. What should I do, I wonder, go deeper and pay a huge time penalty? Or wait? I decide to wait.

The incandescent ache begins to ease. My leg muscles quiver with relief. I lie down, shut my eyes and try to relax. A new voice comes over the intercom. "How are you feelin', Doc?" It is my old friend Frank, a professional diver taking his turn as the chamber operator.

"Better, Frank, much better. Thanks."

"Good. Now you take it easy, Doc. We can't afford to have you traumatized. Otherwise who's goin' to look after us during the midnight pub crawl?"

I picture a group of white-coated men standing beside him. Bill Hamilton. Heinz Schreiner. Pat Kelly. They will be deep in conversation about the future course of the decompression. They will be talking about the depth and the time of the accident and the condition of the diver. They will be considering optional gas mixtures. These and other factors will be reduced to numbers and estimates. The original matrix will be studied. A new schedule with longer stops, slower ascents and different breathing gases will be constructed.

For the first time, I am beginning to understand a little of what it is like to be an extreme-depth diver who inhabits an alien, unpredictable world. His body sometimes fails him. He lives through moments when he must depend completely on the thoughts and actions of other men.

The intercom crackles. "We're going to maintain you at this depth for an hour. We'll slowly increase the partial pressure of oxygen. Keep drinking liquids so you don't get dehydrated." The voice pauses as if listening to someone else. "Heinz and Pat will reprogram the computer. At the end of an hour, we should have a new decompression schedule. Then we'll start up again."

I nod in agreement and take a long drink of water. The pain in both knees has diminished to a tiny electric twinge.

Morgan puts a hand on my shoulder. "I'm glad you had them turn around when you did," he says. "My left knee was getting pretty sore. I was going to speak up, but you beat me to it."

I look into Morgan's eyes. If he is telling the truth, he has made a generous gesture. If he is lying, he has made a life-long friend.

Dinner arrives through the air lock. Potatoes and roast beef are lying on paper plates curved to fit the small space. Behind them are two small paper cups brimming with red wine.

Some time tomorrow morning, I hope my rubber knees will carry me out through the main hatch. The hours ahead contain a long road up through the shallow depths, breathing pure oxygen through a rubber face mask. The mask will abrade my skin and the oxygen will burn my lungs. There will be the continuing threat of more pain.

But for now I am comfortable. The food is good and the first sip of wine is riding well. Morgan is already asleep. I close the book that has fallen open again on his chest and silently thank him for the little white lies that angels tell.

ELEVEN

SEPTEMBER 1967. It is a chilly fall evening on the western North Atlantic. Under layers of slate-gray clouds, a large, red-painted Canadian Coast Guard ship, the *John Cabot,* turns into the breaking waves, slows her engines and glides to a stop. Two hundred yards off her bow is a U.S. Navy salvage ship, the USS *Utina.* On the horizon are the black outlines of three Russian fishing trawlers operated by Russian military intelligence. Their engines are idling and their radio antennae are aimed at the *Cabot.*

The *Cabot* is a new cable-laying ship five stories high and as long as a football field. Behind her white superstructure are a helicopter hangar and a 40-ton cargo crane. In a steel cradle under the crane is a small yellow submarine. *Deep Diver* is 22 feet long, weighs eight and a half tons and can operate at a depth of 1,300 feet.

Deep Diver is Ed Link's latest invention. In 1965, he took a hard look at the Navy's *SeaLab* program, Cousteau's *Conshelf* projects and his own *Man-in-Sea* program and realized there was a critical area no one had considered: diver mobility.

He explained it this way. "Stenuit and Lindbergh were tied to the station by their hoses and restricted to a radius of a few hundred feet. If their base was a small, ship-mounted sub, they could live and work anywhere on the continental shelf."

Collaborating with submarine builder John Perry, Link designed a sub to carry a pilot and observer in a forward compartment and two divers in a separate diving chamber that could be compressed to 1,250 feet. The chamber, with a hatch that opens to the sea, has all the life-safety systems needed for long, deep dives.

Deep Diver, the world's first diver lock-out research sub. *(Courtesy of Glen Loates)*

I am crouched on the floor of the forward compartment next to the pilot. It's the world's first sub that can park on the bottom, let divers swim out to work and then decompress them, but it's so jammed with instruments and equipment that my knees are touching my chin.

Roger Cook is *Deep Diver*'s pilot. The 25-year-old former member of the U.S. Navy's elite SEAL team is sitting on a short stool with his head and shoulders inside a round conning tower with six small view ports. Within easy reach are a steering wheel, rudder pedals and rows of switches, motors, dials, circuit breakers, black buttons, red buttons, depth indicators, alarm lights, rotary switches and latches with covers so critical they must not be touched by accident. Cook has finished his pre-dive checklist and is glancing at the sky through the forward view ports. He does not like what he sees. The clouds and ocean have lost their color. The only things clearly visible are the white summits of breaking waves.

I look at the two Ocean Systems divers sitting behind us in the diving chamber, a pressure-resistant sphere about six feet in diameter. It has view ports, oxygen lines and sensors, and a carbon dioxide scrubber. Both men are dressed in heavy wool underwear and thick rubber suits. Their helmets and coiled hoses are on the aluminum bench beside them. Their feet rest on the circular hatch that allows them access to the sea.

Denny Breese is 27 years old with a quicksilver smile. A former electronic technician, Breese made 10 patrols in nuclear attack submarines, spending months under the ocean surrounded by weapon control consoles, gleaming racks of torpedoes and a hundred other men. He is an expert on *Deep Diver*'s diving chamber. Vince Taylor is a year older than Breese and works for Ocean Systems in Morgan City. Taylor's normal line of work is swimming out of a diving bell in the Gulf of Mexico at 400 feet and doing whatever it takes to repair a buried gas pipeline.

Cook's feet move back and forth on the rudder pedals. He is anxious to get in the water before darkness obscures the waves. He looks down, sees me writing in my notebook, but says nothing. Then, without warning, everything shudders. The 40-ton crane with its long lift cable picks us up.

As soon as the sub is airborne, it begins to swing. It starts slowly, a gentle back-and-forth motion in time with the roll of the ship, but each swing adds more speed. On the deck below us, men holding white nylon lines attached to the sub try to dampen the motion, but *Deep Diver* slews sideways. Through the forward view ports I see the lights of the helicopter hangar veer into view and then disappear.

I press my face up against a view port and my breath condenses on its cold surface. For an instant, my eyes are level with the steel frame of the sub's support cradle. Then, as we are moved toward the side of the ship, the sub lurches forward and to the right, just missing the *Cabot*'s starboard railing. I catch a glimpse of the men in the deck crew, who are staring at us as if witnessing a hanging.

There is a muted shriek of straining metal as the cable lowers us foot by foot. I look up. High above the rolling tip of the crane, the clouds separate to reveal the curve of the moon. A second later, it is gone.

For the past two years, we have operated *Deep Diver* in the warm waters of the Caribbean, with Link's new hydraulic crane picking us up from the deck of *Sea Diver* and smoothly transferring us into the ocean. Now we are hanging on cable like a wingless aircraft over water as cold as a glacier.

A big wave sweeps under the sub and turns white against the hull of the ship. Cook is up on his feet, his legs bent, his head and shoulders braced against the side of the sub. Through the view ports behind him, I see the ship stretch out like a huge unlit building.

"Stand by," he says through his teeth. "They're going to drop us into the next wave." We wait expectantly, but the crane operator's timing is off. The next wave surges into the sub's belly and falls away. The sub spins wildly. I look down and see water boiling across the lower view ports.

As soon as *Deep Diver* is immersed in the crown of the ocean, the lift cable goes slack and two Navy divers in black wet suits jump out of an inflatable boat, land on the flat section of the hull behind our conning tower and unhook us. We are free of the cable. Then they leap back through broken water into their boat.

The sub pitches down and heaves to the left. There is a dull clang of steel meeting steel. The waves are driving us into the side of the *Cabot*.

Cook spins the wheel and applies full power to the main motor. Our stern propeller whirls and we slide away from the ship. He turns the wheel again and brings the sub around until it is facing into the waves. We pitch up and down; the rolling slows.

Cautiously, I unwrap my body from the steel curve of the pressure sphere. My fingers are stiff and bloodless. My heart is thumping. I glance around to make sure nothing is loose.

During this dive, my job is to control the pressure and composition of the breathing gases in both compartments. I check the oxygen sensor and the oxygen flow meter. Both are normal, but I check them again.

I study the carbon dioxide sensor and the amount of air flowing through the carbon dioxide scrubber. Then I place my fingers on its metal cover to make sure it isn't hot. Two years ago in Washington, two Navy divers were in a chamber at the Experimental Diving Unit when their scrubber overheated and caught fire, filling the chamber with flames and thick, black smoke. Within minutes, they were killed by smoke inhalation.

As the sub continues to pitch up and down, I look closely at Cook, Breese and Taylor. They are bright, inventive men willing to endure sleepless nights and whatever else it takes to tear apart any one of the sub's electronic, hydraulic or mechanical systems, repair it and put it back together again. They are midnight experts in the art of scrounging and manufacturing spare parts. Much of my admiration for them comes from their bawdy sense of humor and the stories that slip out so easily after a few drinks—the rogue shark seen at 200 feet off the coast of Africa, the wildcat well that blew out in the Amazon delta or the pipeline welding accident that caved in the chests of two of their friends in Alaska.

Cook checks the trim in the forward ballast tank, tests a pair of power circuits and picks up the phone to talk to the surface support team. I suspect that the line is being monitored by Russian hydrophones. On the *Cabot,* in a corner of the helicopter hangar, three men in yellow slickers are huddled over an underwater radio, listening to Cook's faint, echoing words. He places the phone back in its slot.

"We're cleared to dive. All set in the dive compartment?"

"Aye. Ready any time."

I glance over my shoulder through the open hatch into the diving chamber. Breese and Taylor are solidly wedged inside a tangle of equipment looking as though they would rather be somewhere else.

Cook reaches down and turns a valve. Air rushes out of a vent and the sub's main ballast tanks begin to fill with water. Slowly, still pitching, the sub slides forward and begins to sink. Twenty seconds later we are below the turbulent surface.

Cook flips a toggle switch and the water in front of the sub fills with a halo of green light and a gauzy curtain of microscopic plants and animals. I have seen plankton before, but in these latitudes, their layers are much denser, part of a vast oceanic pasture that feeds cod, herring and mackerel.

"They've given us a compass bearing to the Navy ship," says Cook. "I'm going to power over in that direction and try to get into position."

Cook levels the sub off at 52 feet. Then he turns almost due north and heads toward the *Utina*. Trailing off her stern deck is a slim black wire leading down into the depths. The wire is hooked into the object we hope to salvage.

The top-secret SOSUS has been under construction since the beginning of the Cold War and will eventually cost $16 billion. For the past month the U.S. Navy and the American intelligence community have been upgrading a section of the system south of Argentia in Newfoundland.

Two weeks ago, the *Cabot* was dragging a big cable-burying plow across the seafloor when its towing bridle snapped. The $2-million plow is now deeply embedded in the sediments somewhere below us. Last week, with the Russian trawlers monitoring their progress, two Navy divers attempted to salvage it, but their diving platform and breathing hoses became entangled in the currents and both men drowned. The next day we received a call from the Navy's Supervisor of Salvage in Washington. Our mission is to dive down, locate the plow and attach a lift wire to its frame so that a recovery team on the *Cabot* can bring it up to the surface.

Until the last hour or so I was reasonably confident we could do it. Off the coast of Florida and in the Bahamas, we've used *Deep Diver* to make observation dives to more than a thousand feet. We've parked on the seafloor and let divers swim out as deep as 430 feet. The sub has even been used for a 24-hour saturation dive. A few months ago, in our research program in the Gulf of Mexico, two divers lived and worked at 636 feet for 48 hours.

There is another reason for my confidence. We have to live up to the reputation gained by Ocean Systems during last year's recovery of an H-bomb off the coast of Spain.

Eighteen months ago, an airborne tanker was refueling a U.S. Air Force B-52 in the sky above the western Mediterranean when one of its engines caught fire. The fire ignited a fuel tank, the B-52 burst into flames and four H-bombs fell out of the sky. Three landed on shore and one splashed into the sea. Within days, twenty-five Navy ships and three thousand men from the U.S. Sixth Fleet assembled off the coast off Palomares, Spain. In Washington, the Supervisor of Salvage directed Ocean Systems to coordinate the search effort. To get the job done as quickly as possible, the company hired 11 major subcontractors and rounded up a small fleet of deep-diving submarines.

In April, the 12-foot-long cylindrical bomb and its nylon parachute were recovered from almost 3,000 feet of water. According to the Navy report, "The operation ... is the largest concentrated underwater search in history, exceeding the number of persons involved, problems overcome and logistic requirements of the remarkable and successful search for the lost submarine *Thresher*."

"I've got the cable in sight," says Cook.

I peer through one of the forward view ports. *Deep Diver*'s floodlights pass through the sea's green filter for about 20 feet before being swallowed by the blackness.

"Look five degrees to the right," says Cook.

I move to another view port. On the outer edge of the light is a vertical black thread. As we come closer I see it slowly swaying back and forth.

"It's loose," says Cook. "I'm going to ask the ship's crew to take up some slack."

Cook is concerned that a loose cable may wrap itself around our bow-thrusters or propeller. He talks to our surface crew and his request is relayed from the *Cabot* to the *Utina*.

After a few minutes the cable begins to straighten. Then it goes slack. *"Deep Diver,"* says a voice on the intercom. *"Utina* says the seas are increasing and they have to maintain slack in the cable to keep it from breaking."

Cook adds more seawater to the main ballast chamber and the sub begins to descend. The cable is directly in front of us. When the currents push the sub to the left or the right, he calmly guides it back on target.

I look at the life-support panel. The needle on our main depth gauge is moving smoothly. Seventy feet. Ninety feet. One hundred and thirty feet.

In the forecourt of light in front of the sub the cable is still visible. Suddenly, a flash of silver emerges and then retreats into the blackness behind it. A large school of fish has been drawn to our lights.

"Three hundred and fifty feet," says Cook. "Fifty more to go." Then, as I watch, the cable sags, straightens and disappears.

"Damn," says Cook. He stops the descent, trims the sub and stares through the forward view ports. The intercom crackles. *"Deep Diver, Utina* informs us that the seas are now running at eight feet and they've had to loosen the cable."

Keeping the sub level, Cook reverses the main motor and backs away. "The last thing we want to do," he says quietly, "is get our butt lassoed by that mother."

I wish I had Cook's icy detachment. During the past two years I have made more than 50 dives in *Deep Diver,* and on every one of them my mind grappled with the thought of the enormous weight of the ocean, the increasing depth and duration of our descents, the unpredictability of over-stressed steel and the delicacy of instruments subjected to corrosion. Each time I picked up a book to review the history of modern mini-sub diving I read about technical complexities, overconfident and sometimes-arrogant behavior and too-frequent mental lapses that led to tragic accidents.

During our three-day journey from Boston to the dive site, Breese told us about one of the early sea trials of *Aluminaut,* a large aluminum sub. She was running submerged in Long Island Sound and was ballasted for salt water. Without warning she entered a giant plume of fresh water flowing in from the Connecticut River. She lost buoyancy and fell toward the bottom. It took a quick sequence of filling buoyancy tanks, dropping ballast weight and applying full vertical power for the pilot to overcome the 3,000 pounds of lost buoyancy and bring the sub safely back to the surface.

Last year, during the search for the H-bomb off the Spanish coast, *Aluminaut* made frequent contact with the soft, muddy bottom thousands of feet below the surface. On one dive, openings in her keel designed to facilitate flooding acted as sediment scoops and added more than a ton of weight to the sub. Once again, the pilot's mechanical insight, swift action and cold sweat saved the crew from becoming anchored to the bottom.

Even the mechanically simple *Trieste* had problems. During one reconnaissance of *Thresher,* there was a severe short circuit in her main propulsion motor. The overload relays failed to open and arced across each other, completely discharging the batteries and melting their cables. All of this happened a short distance away from *Trieste*'s huge gasoline tanks. If the electronic fireworks had taken place on the surface they might have been the high-voltage overture to a 46,000-gallon explosion.

I look around the dimly lit interior of *Deep Diver.* A small measure of my dread lies within the psychology of submarines. Each vehicle, with its glimmering rows of instruments, radios, scanners, monitors and readouts, depending on the state of the sea and the savvy of the pilot, exhibits its own flaws, mechanical difficulties and illusions of personality. Of all the possible malfunctions, one of the most serious is fire.

Every working sub has a small octopus of wires and cables behind every control panel and display board, part of a network running from the main batteries through pressure hull penetrators into step-down transformers and junction boxes and then to every light dial, button and switch. There may be a quarter of a mile of wiring inside *Deep Diver* and hundreds of electrical connections, and if one of them overheats there will be a small red glow and a whisker of gray smoke. What happens next depends on chance and the reflexes of the pilot. With luck, the fire will extinguish itself. But if something unforeseeable like poor workmanship conducts the combustion into a neighboring nexus of wires, then all kinds of strange things—short circuits or a stream of sparks— might occur. If the fire gets really serious, the smoke and the flames will quickly invade the lungs of the crew.

In January of this year, at the Kennedy Space Center, a machine-made inferno burned its way into the world's consciousness. At 6:30 in the evening, astronauts Ed White, Gus Grissom and Roger Chaffee were lying inside the Apollo Command Module on top of the *Saturn V* rocket. They were strapped into their couches wearing pressure suits and breathing pure oxygen, running through a routine checklist, when without warning there was a yellow flash, a dull orange glow and the muffled sound of voices inside helmets. When the technicians opened the main hatch they found three asphyxiated corpses inside a hideously charred cockpit.

I look up at Cook. "Why don't we forget the cable? If we drop straight down we should be within range of the plow."

Cook hesitates. "It's a long shot, but let's give it a try."

As Cook informs the surface crew, I recheck the oxygen sensor and flow meter. The sensor reads 20.6 percent and the flow meter confirms that oxygen is being added at the same rate we are consuming it.

A strange buff-colored light appears in the lower view ports. "Bottom in sight," says Cook.

The depth gauge reads 410 feet. As our descent slows, I look out across an undulating plain of sediment. We have arrived on the floor of the Grand Banks.

The Banks are an eastward extension of the North American continental shelf, an immense submerged plateau southeast of Newfoundland. They run 450 miles east to west and 350 miles north to south, and are covered with water that has a maximum depth of 600 feet.

These submerged highlands are at the crossroads of two great ocean currents, the Gulf Stream, which passes along the eastern edge, and the cold Labrador Current, which envelopes the greater part of the plateau. Because of this, the Banks are the greatest fishing grounds in the world.

Fishermen have been coming out here in their boats for 300 years, battling the severe storms, thick fog and icebergs brought down by the Labrador Current. We are the first to see the hidden land that lies beneath their nets.

This is a place of awe and imagining. Somewhere out there are hundreds of downed ships and the faint molecular remains of the men, women and children who were once on them. And somewhere over the southern edge of the Grand Banks is the shattered hull of the Mount Everest of shipwrecks, RMS *Titanic*.

With the sound of steel nudging stone, we touch down gently on the seafloor. The sub leans slightly to one side and then rights itself. A swirling brown cloud rises up from below and dims the view ports. I try looking out, but the only thing I see is the soft light of an instrument panel reflecting off the glass.

"This is weird country," says Cook.

We wait until the sediment drifts away in vertical strands. Off to the right, on the edge of our lights, a school of northern cod strokes the current with slow-moving tails. Their round eyes turn to gaze in our direction. I press my fingertips against the cold steel that keeps us at the same pressure as the surface of the sea. I am in a place where distances are greater than they seem. In spite of their closeness, the silver fish are as remote as the Precambrian ocean.

"What the hell ..." Cook's eyes are focused on a brown cloud forming off to our left. Something thin and black springs out of it and is gone.

"It's the damn cable. It's kicking up the mud on the bottom."

Cook puts the sub into reverse and we move back about 30 feet. Then he leans his shoulder against the pressure hull and takes a deep breath. He has seen discarded communication cables lying in coils on the ocean floor. He has seen trans-ocean telephone cables suspended off the bottom and camouflaged by sediment. This is the first time he has come face to face with a wire that is alive and thrashing the water.

The research sub *Deep Diver* with a diver swimming to the work site. (*Courtesy of Glen Loates*)

We sit listening to the hum of fans, blowers and pumps. My thoughts are of a night that lasts forever.

After a full minute, a voice comes out of the darkness of the diving chamber. "Perhaps," says Breese, "the way to avoid a lethal bite from the super snake is to approach the plow from the other side."

Cook gives Breese a conspirator's smile. "Let's give it a try." He checks his compass heading and then using the main motor and rudder begins to crab the sub along a roughly semi-circular course.

Once we locate the plow, we will make a quick survey to find its best attachment point. Then we will park next to it and close the hatch into the diving chamber. When Taylor and Breese are ready, they will add oxygen-helium to their compartment until it equals the water pressure outside. Then the hatch beneath their feet will drop open. While Breese stays inside, Taylor will swim over to the plow and attach the lift line. If there are no hitches, the dive should take about 30 minutes.

When Taylor swims back in, he will secure the hatch behind him. As soon as the sub leaves the surface, I will begin to decompress the divers by bleeding off the pressure inside their compartment. We will finish the six-hour decompression back on board the ship.

As Cook nears the completion of his half-circle excursion, I try to locate the plow by using the sub's electronic direction finder. I tune in to the acoustic signal coming from the plow and rotate a dial that is supposed to indicate the compass heading we should take. In spite of my efforts, every direction yields the same unproductive shriek.

I look over my shoulder at the divers. Breese is checking a fitting on his helmet. Taylor is looking out a view port and frowning. "We'd better find that iron lady soon," he says.

"This is it, Vince," says Cook. "I'm going to put you right on top of it."

Cook tilts our bow up and we begin to inch forward. From some-where below comes the sound of steel passing over stone. Once again I put on the earphones and try to dial in the direction of the acoustic signal coming from the plow. My ears fill with an ear-numbing sound. At such close range, the device must be paralyzed.

I look out a forward view port. We are a few feet above the seafloor moving across a wilderness. There are isolated rocks and small islands of vegetation. Pale crabs scuttle into and out of our lights. We pass over a swath of seafloor that has been clear-cut by a deep-sea fishing dredge. The bottom is flat and lifeless.

Up ahead, a brown cloud appears in the green edge of our lights. "Damn," says Cook. "We've missed it. We're back where we started." He stops the sub and lets her settle to the bottom. Mud rises up and covers the view ports.

When Cook looks at me with his level green eyes, I hope he can't see my fear. If we get snagged in the cable and the men in the *Utina* can't break it loose from the plow, we are going to turn into a permanent fixture on the floor of the Grand Banks.

The intercom crackles. "*Deep Diver,* request you surface immediately. Repeat. Surface immediately. The winds are at 30 knots and rising." Seconds pass as each of us responds to the fact that we are going to exchange one thick adrenaline moment on the bottom for another on the surface.

"Well," cracks Breese in a fake falsetto, "it's been nice masquerading as a diver for these past few hours. Since I don't get to swim, no one will know the enormous range of my deepwater talents. Remember the old Navy diver's oath. We dive for five ..." He rambles on, prying the lid off the tension.

Cook turns and looks at each of us. "Roger, topside," he says slowly into the intercom. "We're on our way up."

He flips a couple of switches and turns a valve that blows compressed air into the ballast chambers. Slowly we begin to ascend.

At 350 feet, the water becomes clearer. As we pass through 200 feet, thin bands of transparent tissue surround us. They swirl in our slipstream and then disappear. The water is filled with a fleet of tiny jellyfish pulsing with rainbow-colored lights. When the sub begins to respond to the turbulence of the waves above us, Cook slows our ascent and holds us at 50 feet.

"*Deep Diver,* this is the *Cabot.* We see your lights off our stern. You are a hundred yards away and clear of all vessels. We urge extreme caution when you come alongside. Winds are gusting to 40 knots. Come to the surface when you're ready."

Taylor's Louisiana drawl eases into the silence. "No sense waitin'. Let's get this mutha airborne."

I press my back against the curve of the pressure sphere, wrap my fingers around a pair of handholds and brace my legs. I have a sudden dislike of confinement and darkness. My eyes yearn for sunlight.

Cook reaches forward and releases a blast of air into our ballast tanks. Our bow tilts and we start upward. Thirty seconds later we burst through the surface like a blue whale breaching and begin to roll in the turmoil of the waves. Water and foam slash across the upper view ports. From the stern I hear the moan of something under tension.

Cook stares over the waves at the blurred outline of the *Cabot* lying parallel to the wind and applies full power to the main propeller. It takes us five minutes to catch the drifting ship. At times we pitch and roll so violently that I can see dark rain clouds through the side view ports. As soon as we enter into the protected lee of the *Cabot,* the violence begins to subside.

Gauging the drift of the *Cabot,* Cook steers us downwind until we are abeam of the recovery crane. Two Navy divers jump onto the flat area behind our conning tower, hook in the lift cable, and leap back into their boat.

I look through an upper view port. To get back up to the helicopter deck we will be lifted 30 feet into an unwelcoming sky. With a faint shudder, the sub rises out of the tangle of waves. Then it begins to swing sideways. At first the motion is comforting, like a child's swing. The side of the ship comes in close and falls away. Down below, the ocean turns into a dark plain of white-edged shadows.

As the sub is pulled upward, the swings become longer. We arc slowly toward the bow, then toward the stern and then back again. At one pause at the end of an arc, I look through a porthole into a room where a sailor is reading.

When we reach the level of the helicopter pad, the crane operator waits until the sub pauses and then edges us sideways until we are over the deck. Four men run in under the sub to attach handling lines, but we fly over their outstretched arms. After three passes, the roll of the ship and the swing of the sub combine and we hesitate in mid-flight. Four white nylon lines are thrown around the sub's yellow frame.

A dozen men run out of the darkness to help with the lines, but the sub is already moving sideways. On one swing the sub's battery pod strikes a line handler on the shoulder, driving him to his knees. Seconds later we almost pass through the open door of the helicopter hangar.

Finally, the men on the deck pull our eight-and-a-half-ton sub into the dark space above its cradle. They call out to the crane operator and we crash into the rubber-coated steel arms. Two men duck under the sides of the sub and secure tie-down cables. A wooden ladder is placed on our starboard side and a sailor in a yellow slicker climbs up to release the lift cable.

I am the last one out. The crane's engine is turned off and the air is filled with the sounds of rain, men's voices and the moan of the wind in the ship's rigging. I climb down the ladder and stand next to the sub. My hands are shaking. My three companions are looking at me with eyes as empty as broken windows. "We're headed back into the Navy base in Argentia," says Cook, as the rain streams off the end of his nose. "The weather's goin' down and the Navy has postponed the mission."

It was the last we heard of it. The mission, like so many carried out at the height of the Cold War, disappeared behind a curtain of military secrecy.

TWELVE

MARCH 1968. It is a warm, windy day and *Sea Diver*'s anchor is set inside a line of patch reefs running parallel to the shore of Grand Bahamas Island. Fifty feet below the keel of the ship is Ed Link's undersea station and, a short swim away, an inflatable black rubber workroom he calls *Igloo*. For the past 10 days, we have been demonstrating how *Deep Diver* can be used to shuttle marine scientists and their equipment down to the seafloor so they can work at depths beyond scuba divers. In a month, the scientists will begin a series of dives to explore the natural history of a submerged escarpment lying west of Nassau.

I make my way toward the stern of the ship, duck under *Deep Diver*'s yellow hull and stand up inside her diving chamber. The air is warm and smells of damp neoprene. The light from a yellow bulb on the top of the chamber falls across the faces of Denny Breese and a heavy-set man talking on a headset. A line of sweat runs across the top of his dark brown mustache.

"Sorry," he says, as he take off the headset, "my film director wanted a last-minute briefing." The steel walls of the diving chamber add luster to his deep, resonant voice.

I run my eyes over his brand-new equipment. A face mask is perched high on his forehead. He is wearing a short-sleeved neoprene wet suit and a weight belt. His swim fins and breathing regulator are placed neatly on the bench beside him.

"Do you need any of this?" I ask, holding out a small tube of Vaseline.

Walter Cronkite touches his mask. "No, thanks, I've already taken care of it."

He has no idea of how much relief his smile gives me; yesterday I almost drowned him.

⬧

Last week Link took me aside and told me that Walter Cronkite wanted to spend two days on *Sea Diver* filming a segment for his television series *The 21st Century.*

"He wants to do a story about the conquest of the continental shelf and make it as authentic as possible. He'd like to make a dive in *Deep Diver* and lock out of her diving chamber."

Link's dark eyes bored into mine. "A lot is at stake here. He's going to share our story with millions of people. I want you to be personally responsible for his safety. Make sure he's physically fit. Show him the skills he needs to make a short, shallow dive."

I spent the next few days sulking around the ship. It is a responsibility I have not asked for and do not want. Walter Cronkite is one of the best-known men in America. Since 1962, he has been the anchorman of the *CBS Evening News.* Every night at six o'clock, 22 million people listen intently as he summarizes the world's most important events. If something goes wrong with his health, I am going to be banished to the outer edge of the ocean.

Cronkite first came to the world's attention as a combat journalist in the Second World War. His career took off when he joined CBS and began reporting the news with a clarity and confidence that were somehow reassuring. Then, sitting in a broadcast booth in the coastal Florida scrub with the latest Mercury-Atlas rocket in the haze behind him, he became the voice of the new American space program. When the rockets rose into the sky on their pillars of flame, he described the pioneering flights of John Glenn, Scott Carpenter and the rest of the "original seven." There is something in his commanding voice and soothing manner that inspires people to call him "the most trusted man in America."

It is a time when America is yearning for trust. Almost half a million troops are fighting in Vietnam. So far, 15,000 soldiers, sailors and airmen have been killed. After years of warfare, all the battles fuse into a blurred image of young GIs in sweat-stained battle gear supported by B-52 bombers, naval guns, tanks and napalm locked in an interminable war with men and women wearing black pajamas and sandals fashioned from old rubber tires. Everyone is wondering why America, with its absurd technological advantages, is so powerless. As the body bags pile up and the enemy filters in from the north, the Pentagon keeps telling the American people, "The war against the Communists is being won every day."

Cronkite's nightly newscasts are filled with graphic stories of horrific battles in Vietnam. As the months pass, he senses that the American military is distorting the truth. Finally, he asks the question that resonates with every American: "What the hell is going on? I thought we were winning." The words sweep across the country and force Americans to realize that the first casualty in any war is the truth.

❖

Teaching Cronkite to dive and ensuring his safety are going to be challenging. The scientists who use *Deep Diver* have made hundreds of scuba dives before they step into the sub. Then we spend hours confirming they know how to use every one of the systems inside the diving chamber.

I have another worry. Walter Cronkite is known as an aggressive reporter. Is he the kind of man who will insist on doing things he shouldn't?

I console myself with the thought that I have always been fascinated with individuals who are making a difference. Men like Cronkite are experts in their fields, with attributes of character I want to understand and perhaps emulate. Whatever happens, Walter Cronkite is going to teach me something.

A few days later, Cronkite flies into Freeport and comes to the ship with his producer, director, soundman, cameraman and an assistant. His dark hair is combed straight back and he's wearing a navy blue T-shirt and sunglasses. His manner is crisp and business-like. When I show him the interior of the sub, he tells me that he has never used scuba equipment but is eager to learn. We agree to meet at two o'clock at the training pool of a nearby resort that specializes in training divers.

In a small room next to the pool, I review his medical history and give him a complete physical examination. He is a big man with a large chest and strong arms. His heart rate and blood pressure are within normal limits.

As I examine him my mind goes back to that November day in 1963 when I saw him on a television screen saying: "From Dallas, Texas, the flash—apparently official. President Kennedy died at 1 P.M. Central Standard Time—a half hour ago."

Whatever he was going to say next stuck in his throat. He gulped twice and tears formed in the corner of his eyes. A few seconds later, he regained his composure. "Vice-President Johnson has left the hospital in Dallas ... presumably he will be taking the oath of office shortly and become the 36th President of the United States." Cronkite is a combat reporter fully engaged with every story he tells.

"Although you're carrying a few extra pounds," I tell him, "there seems to be no medical reason why you shouldn't dive. Can you think of any?"

He slips his T-shirt back over his head and gives me a level look. "As a journalist, most of my work is done in a chair. This is one of those times when I get out of the chair. What do we do next?"

The training pool is a concrete tower two stories high, with thick walls and large observation windows. As part of my evaluation of Cronkite's physical condition, I have him pick up all his gear—masks, fins, weight belt, regulator and full air cylinder—and climb its two flights of stairs to the upper deck. Halfway up, he pauses for a few seconds, but when we reach the top he is breathing normally for this kind of exertion.

I start by describing how the sub will be launched over the stern of the ship and land on the seafloor. Then I tell him what he has to do to get outside. "Denny Breese will be the safety diver in the chamber with you. He'll take you through every step."

"How do you make sure the sub stays on the bottom?" he asks bluntly.

"The pilot will add enough ballast so the sub is about 200 pounds negative."

Starting with the face mask, I describe each piece of diving equipment and tell him what he has to do to make it work.

"How do you control your buoyancy underwater?"

"How cold is the water?"

"What kind of light will we have down there?"

"What do I do if I run out of air?"

As the questions come one after the other, it becomes clear that Walter Cronkite is one of those men who try to figure out everything in advance.

"How do I equalize the pressure on my eardrums?"

"When the pressure increases, hold your nose and blow—gently," I reply. "Start as soon you feel the air coming into the chamber. Keep blowing as you descend."

"How do I avoid gas embolism?" The question confirms I am talking to a reporter who has done his homework.

"When you are breathing on the regulator," I say, "exhale fully each time. Never hold your breath—especially as you come up to the surface."

To evaluate his confidence in the water, I ask him to put on his swim fins and face mask and swim a few laps of the pool. He pushes off, trailing his arms at his side, letting his legs do the work of pushing him through the water.

My confidence is growing by the minute. This is a man who flew to Vietnam, put on a steel helmet and army fatigues, and went to the front line with a camera and microphone. He'll do whatever it takes to get his story.

He's ready for the final step. I put a scuba tank on his back, position a weight belt around his waist and help him secure the buckles. He slips into the water and holds on to the side of the pool while I gear up and join him.

"Start breathing from the regulator and let's give it a try."

Cronkite places his mouthpiece between his lips and begins breathing. He adjusts to the feeling of air coming through a mouthpiece into his lungs and slowly pushes away from the side of the pool. He floats for a few seconds, exhales and sinks like a stone.

I swim down, grab the top of his tank and haul him to the surface. He calmly removes his mouthpiece and turns toward me. "That felt like an elevator ride to the basement." He is breathing rapidly. As he takes off his face mask, water trickles out from under its lower skirt.

"I'm sorry. It's my fault. I gave you too much weight." I remove four pounds of lead and reposition his belt around his waist.

Cronkite pushes back from the edge of the pool, exhales and drops out of sight. I slip below the surface and follow him down. Despite some water in his mask, he seems to be doing fine. I glance over at Chuck Peterson, an underwater photographer taking pictures. When I turn around, Cronkite is gone. I look up. He is on the surface. Peterson points to the bottom. Lying in a heap is Cronkite's blue canvas weight belt. My God, I think, I'm going to kill the most trusted man in America. I swim down, put the weight belt over my arm, and make my way to the top of the pool.

"What was *that* all about?" says Cronkite. There is an exclamation mark after each word.

"I'm really sorry." My voice is barely audible. "The buckle on your weight belt must have come loose."

"I'm learning a lot about going down and coming up. I'd like to see what it's like to stay down." His voice has dropped an octave.

"This time I'll make sure your belt doesn't come undone."

I help Cronkite tighten his buckle and pray that no one has been below watching this through one of the observation windows.

After catching his breath, Cronkite makes his way over to a stainless steel ladder and eases himself down rung by rung. He is breathing effortlessly. He discovers that by exhaling gently, he can descend and that by kicking his fins, he can ascend. There is only one problem. His face mask keeps filling with water.

He swims back up to the edge of the pool and I tighten his mask. Once again he descends. I position myself directly in front of him and look into his mask. At about five feet, water begins to creep up both sides of his nose heading toward his eyelids. I guide him back to the surface. He takes off his mask and shakes his head. "Damn, it's my mustache. It's leaking like a screen door."

I look at the neatly trimmed rectangle of brown hair on his upper lip. "You're right. Your mustache is preventing the skirt of your mask from making a complete seal against your skin. Let's try another mask."

It doesn't work. Then we attempt to adjust the mask so that it rides above his mustache. Again, it floods. I look into the man's eyes, measure his gaze and ask a question that I regret as soon as the words leave my mouth. "How badly do you want to make this dive?"

He glares at me. "I'm telling a story about America's new frontiers, including space and the ocean. I've got to tell the ocean's story from the inside, using the latest technology. Let's work on a solution."

I look at his mustache and stare at his mask. I am learning that in any challenge, understanding the small details, especially the ones right in front of you, makes all the difference.

The frown on Cronkite's face suggests that it is time to lighten up.

"There's a surgical answer to this problem," I say. "Why don't we get a razor and some shaving cream and amputate the mustache?"

"That's not an option. The damn thing's insured for a million bucks." He is smiling.

"I've got an idea," says Peterson, who is in the water beside us. He gets out of the pool, opens his dive bag and hands me a small tube of Vaseline. "If it's good enough to seal an O-ring, it should work on a mustache."

I spread a thin layer on the hair below Cronkite's nose and reposition his mask. He pushes away from the side of the pool and descends. For the next 20 minutes he makes the deep pool his own, dropping down to the bottom, inspecting all four of its corners, and pausing at one of its underwater windows to look out at the sunlit lagoon to the west.

❖

In the research sub's diving chamber, Cronkite makes a last-minute check of his scuba gear and the life-support systems. "You've crammed a lot of teaching into the last 24 hours—any last-minute advice?"

"Just the things we emphasized yesterday," I say. "Equalize your ears early and often. Breathe in and out slowly. Don't hold your breath."

Just before the sub is launched over *Sea Diver*'s stern, I put on my diving gear, step over the side of the ship, descend and come to a stop next to *Igloo*. The water is blue-green and clear. Overhead, silhouetted by the sun, is the purple outline of *Sea Diver*.

A few minutes later, *Deep Diver* lands softly on the sand. I hear the hum of its small maneuvering propellers and water flooding into its trim tanks. A CBS cameraman swims toward the sub and positions himself a few feet away from the rear hatch. Three minutes later the hatch opens and Cronkite's finned feet appear. He plants his fins on the sand, ducks out from under the sub and stands up. He does a full 360-degree turn, looking at the sub and the seafloor with evident fascination.

Yesterday I asked him what he thought was the most important story he had reported on during his career. "A century from now, the story that will be remembered is how humans escaped from their earthly environment—and began to live in space and inside the sea."

Denny Breese drops out of the sub and spends a full minute checking Cronkite's equipment. Side by side, with air bubbles streaming from their regulators, they swim over to inspect the station.

Over the past day, as he absorbed the essentials of undersea technology, Walter Cronkite was transformed by it. He has interviewed Ed Link, talked to almost everyone on the ship and learned how our machines work. For the moment, after stepping out of his underwater taxi, he is an air-breathing earthling exploring another world through the marvels of twentieth-century ingenuity.

※

His television special is broadcast several months later and is accurate and authentic. It shows how life-safety technologies, including *Deep*

A diver coming out of Ed Link's inflatable rubber workstation during
Walter Cronkite's lock-out dive from *Deep Diver*. *(Courtesy of Glen Loates)*

Ed Link (left) and the author on top of *Deep Diver*.

The author sitting between Robert Stenuit (left) and Jon Lindbergh
during decompression from their "deepest, longest dive."

The author helping Clay Link adjust the lift chain on top of the submersible decompression chamber.

The author emerging from the decompression chamber after his 650-foot dive.

The research sub *Deep Diver* being recovered from the ocean and placed on the deck of the cable-laying vessel *John Cabot*.

Astronaut/aquanaut Scott Carpenter preparing to make a practice dive in San Francisco harbor.

SeaLab 3 aquanauts on their daily two-mile morning run.
The author is second from the right in the back row.

Philippe Cousteau, 1969.

The *SeaLab 3* undersea station being modified
at the U.S. Naval Shipyard in San Francisco.

SeaLab 3 being launched into the Pacific off San Clemente Island.

The author in a wet suit, putting on a *SeaLab 3* helmet before a practice dive in San Francisco harbor.

Divers about to enter *Sublimnos,* Canada's first underwater station, on the bottom of Lake Huron.

Apollo 11 on its launch pad the night before liftoff to the moon.

Pierre Trudeau diving to the *Tektite 2* undersea station in the U.S. Virgin Islands.

Deep Rover 2 being launched over the side of the *Ares* at the Lost City vent site.

Producer-director James Cameron (left) and the author on the deck of the *Ares*.

Diver and Link's undersea station, are making the exploration of "inner space" possible. It hints at the brooding, barely recognized forces lying under the surface, waiting to ambush the unwary. Like the other programs in the series, it reinforces the core belief that Americans, through intelligence and hard work, can master any circumstance.

THIRTEEN

JULY 1968. In a humid twilight filled with mosquitoes, I climb up the gangway of the rusting supply vessel and head across its deck toward the dive chamber. The water beside the ship looks like scorched molasses. At the end of the pier, a neon Budweiser sign flashes on and off, its light reflecting in the road made wet by a rain that has just stopped.

It is a road that slices through the Louisiana tidelands from Morgan City to the Gulf of Mexico, an endless blur of swamp-forest, scrub-shrub, bay heads and tidal marsh winding across the Mississippi Delta until it runs out in this end-of-the-world collection of gray-plank, tin-roof buildings. The smell of dead fish and diesel exhaust assaults my nostrils.

"Ova heah, Doc." A giant, bare-armed diver in oil-stained denim coveralls beckons me to the far end of the chamber. I step over a coil of air hose, duck under a makeshift canvas roof, cup my hands around my eyes, and look through a view port into the chamber.

The diver I have come to treat is lying on his back under the glare of a light bulb. He is a big man in his thirties, completely naked except for a pair of wrinkled skivvies. He has a beard that hasn't seen a razor in days. His eyes are closed and his mouth is open. A crimson line runs from his lower lip into the curve of his neck. He does not appear to be breathing.

"I better get in there fast. What's his depth?"

"Hun'red feet, Doc."

I walk down the length of the chamber. There is no wind, only the withering, mangrove-scented, 90-degree heat. Beyond the stern of the vessel, the Gulf of Mexico reflects the night's first stars on its silvery surface. The two divers beside me are half a foot taller than I am.

"Ah'm Randall," says one. "Smitty," grunts the other. Their strong handshakes send a sliver of pain into my wrist.

As soon as the hatch closes behind me a voice crackles out of the intercom. "Y'all ready? Gonna drop you fast."

The pressure comes so quickly, I hardly have time to clear my ears. In less than a minute, I am at 100 feet pushing the inner hatch open into a lighted space that stinks of stale sweat and vomit.

DC Ferris has large, full ears and black hair curling down the back of his neck. There are scabs and skin burns on the front of his thighs. When I place my palm an inch above his open mouth, it is impossible to tell if he is breathing.

"Y'all gonna say a rosary for him, Doc?" says the intercom. Unblinking eyes stare through the view ports.

In the race from Morgan City to get here, I sat on the passenger bench of a 1960 Ford pickup, my feet braced against the floor boards, listening carefully to the Ocean Systems dive supervisor as he sped along at 90 miles an hour.

"The call came in jus' before we found you in the shop. The boys bin six days out in the Gulf jettin' in a pipe to a production platform. DC was workin' the jet pump at 66 feet when he ran into a snarl of Haliburton wi-ar."

"What is Haliburton wire?"

"It's a real thin wi-ar used by drillin' crews. Thick as a pencil lead, but you caint cut it. Sometimes, when it kinks, the crews toss the whole mess into the ocean. Could be as much as ten thousand feet long, an' when it lands on the seafloor it gathers itself into a man-eatin' coil."

He swerves the truck past the humped shell of a gopher tortoise on the rain-slicked road.

"With the mud'n'all, the visibility was less'n four feet. So the rescue diver couldn't find ol' DC. Took two hours to get him free of that mutha-fuckin wi-ar. We almost lost the rescue diver."

"What happened next?"

"Boys kinda lost track of things after that. No time to write things down. Best ah kin tell, they popped ol' DC to the surface, tossed him in the chamber, dropped him to a hun'red feet and called us. Good thing you was in town, Doc."

I survey the chamber. The man lying on the mat in front of me is so big there is barely room for both of us on the floor. Other than his size, the most prominent feature of his anatomy is a giant wave of flesh that strains against the frayed elastic of his undershorts. Since no one knows exactly what happened during his dive, it is impossible to tell how he arrived at his present condition. Is he suffering from air embolism or decompression sickness? Has he had a heart attack? Fortunately for any examining physician whose heart is jogging furiously, the art of medicine has the comfort of ritual.

I begin to explore the mystery of DC's medical status by reaching for his wrist and finding his pulse. I will measure its rate and then listen to the sounds of his heart. I will gently feel his limbs for broken bones. These time-honored steps give me time to review what little I know about his personal history.

DC, or "Direct Current" as he is sometimes called, was hired three months ago. He's a hot-tap welder from Baton Rouge who spent his first month with the company working on a pipeline about 50 miles offshore. He is one of those divers who can light up a 5,000-degree welding torch at 200 feet, control its fire and burn two ends of a pipe together in a matter of minutes. According to the dive supervisor, DC is a "cowboy" who takes unnecessary risks.

Like most of the commercial divers working under the Gulf of Mexico, DC is as tough as corrosion-proof steel. One night he was climbing up a ladder on an oil rig, lost his footing on a grease slick, fell 15 feet and draped his body over a bollard. He lay in this position for so long the tool pusher ran to the communications room to call for a helicopter to fly him to the hospital. Before he came back, DC got up, dusted off his coveralls and asked why everybody was staring at him.

I asked the supervisor if DC had any medical problems. He told me there were none that he knew of except a terminal addiction to Camel cigarettes and high-test bourbon. About a month ago, DC interrupted his in-water decompression to swim up to the surface, duck out of his helmet and grab a quick smoke. The supervisor asked him just what the hell he thought he was doing. "Jus' airin' out my lungs," was the reply. Two quick puffs and he headed back down into the depths.

Bourbon has a similar hold on him. Sometimes after a long, hard dive, DC will finish his in-water decompression, climb the ladder up to the barge, strip off his helmet and heavy gear, step into the chamber, and reach for a silver flask hidden in his socks. When he's ashore he often starts drinking at noon.

"DC, can you hear me?"

His eyelids flicker, but remain closed.

"DC, are you OK?"

DC slowly turns his head to one side revealing a soiled T-shirt and a crushed pack of Camels. I reach down, pull out a cigarette and hold it under his nose.

"DC, can you hear me?"

The head turns back and the eyelids flutter open. DC's eyeballs are bloodshot, but his pupils are normal in size.

"How come you here, man? You must be here for something." The slurred words are stuck together like taffy.

I spend the next 20 minutes confirming that I have a patient who is in reasonably stable condition but can't give an accurate account of what happened during his dive. He's got a steady pulse of 62 beats a minute and his blood pressure is normal. From what I can see he weighs about 220 pounds, much of it fat. The fingers and palms of his huge hands are crosshatched with barnacle cuts. He doesn't remember falling, so there is a reasonable chance that the pain in his right knee is from decompression sickness. He says that he was drinking heavily the night before and was hung over when he showed up for work. He breathed pure oxygen for an hour before his dive. "Didn't help ma head much," he said. "Jus' made me dizzy."

I ask the divers outside to add an additional 30 feet of pressure to our depth. Two minutes later, DC tells me that the pain in his knee is going away.

The temperature inside the chamber feels like a runaway sauna. There is a quick way to eliminate at least 50 watts of heat.

"Can you switch off the interior light and shine a flashlight through one of the ports? And will you send down some water and wet towels?"

As soon as the light goes out DC closes his eyes and begins to snore softly. Following some ancient instinct, a big cockroach emerges from a fold in DC's T-shirt, ambles across the sweat-stained mattress and disappears down a hole in the steel floor grating.

Because DC has spent at least eight hours at 100 feet, I decide to treat him as if all his tissues are fully saturated. I ask the divers to begin decompressing the chamber at the rate of 12 minutes per foot, warning them to prepare for the more than 24 hours it will take to get us back to the surface. They tell me they are going to get three men to drive down from Morgan City and give them a hand.

Since my first trip to Louisiana two years ago, I have developed a great affection for the big, raw-boned men who work the deep water off this wild, tideland coast. They live in Morgan City or in small towns in nearby parishes. Many of them are Cajuns, descendents of the Acadians from Nova Scotia who migrated to Louisiana during the American Revolution. They are intelligent, lecherous, loud laughing and serious with a natural caution. They know about injury and death at sea in its most surprising and painful aspects. But there are many among them who love to flirt with danger.

Most of them never completed high school, but the risks they take earn them as much as $50,000 a year. The money lingers in their pockets for a very short time before it is converted into late-model pickup trucks, hunting gear and 3,000-watt stereo systems. A lot of their cash ends up as an endless flow of beer, rum and bourbon downed in swift, throat-numbing gulps.

Their workplace is the oil-rich Gulf of Mexico, with its more than 300 offshore rigs and platforms in constant need of underwater repair and maintenance. Their home ashore is a subtropical world of moss-draped live oaks, shrimp boats and shipbuilding yards flanking the wide, mud-brown Atchafalaya River. They live and work in a world drowned in 65 inches of rain every year.

When they are not working, they frequent bait shops and eat fried catfish and sweet-water crabs. In the cypress swamps that begin a hundred yards beyond the outskirts of town, they can be seen wearing thick boots, carrying military rifles and dodging snakes as they hunt raccoons, muskrat and alligators. Their on-again, off-again relationships with women keep them in a constant state of heartbreak.

They do not consider the wider world. It is not a matter of ignorance but of intensity. They have room in their heads for diving and nothing else. When they fly in from the oil rigs to spend a few days on shore, they seek comfort in any activity that protects them against the hazards of their work.

Their work is centered on two kinds of diving. "Bounce" dives are descents of two hours or less to make an inspection or recover lost equipment. "Saturation" dives are used for long-duration welding or construction jobs. They have learned what they know about saturation diving from the U.S. Navy and our studies in the Buffalo research facility. The dive team lives, sometimes for days at a time, in a pressurized chamber on a work barge. Each morning they transfer to a diving bell and commute to work by being lowered into the water for an eight-hour shift.

I wake DC and try to get him to drink.

"You've lost a lot of water from sweating. You've got to replace it."

"Ah bet you're a good doctor, huh?" He props himself up on one elbow and tries to drink from a paper cup. "Ah bet you graduated smart."

"You've got to drink more than that."

"Can't, Doc. It tastes terrible. Needs some fire."

"Fire?"

DC reaches into the pocket of a wrinkled pile of blue denim and pulls out a silver flask.

"DC, I can't let you do that."

"Ah know you can't, so that's why ah'm doing it." He pours a few drops into the cup and downs it in one gulp. He follows it with another. The faces in the view ports are smiling.

Hours pass. DC sleeps. To give him as much room as possible, I sit at one end of the chamber with my knees tucked under my chin. I try to stay awake, but the stifling heat closes my eyes.

❖

In the place between consciousness and sleep, I relive the first time I walked through the door of Lil's Elbow Room, the bar Morgan City's commercial divers call their own. It is almost midnight and dark enough to be 50 fathoms under the sea. Tonight, like every night, the music is loud and the bar is crowded with men with cropped hair and smoldering eyes surrounded by clouds of cigarette smoke. We have just flown in from a rig 80 miles out in the Gulf and money and celebration are in the air.

"Come ovah heah, Doc. You gotta see this," says Big Lyle.

Big Lyle is the first diver I treated on the ocean off Louisiana. After I rode a helicopter out to the rig at 4 A.M. to bring him and his crushed leg to the Morgan City hospital, he said he would take care of me when we got back on shore. "You the first flyin'-divin' doc in the Mississippi Delta, an' you small enough to be an alligator snack. Somebody's gonna have to look after your skinny northern ass in Morgan City, an' it may as well be me."

Big Lyle is 6 foot 5 inches and has muscles in places where most men don't have places. He walks with a limp, but the calf of his leg, compressed to red jelly between a storm-tossed supply ship and the landing platform of the oil rig, is healing well.

We make our way into a crowd of men with glasses in their hands. Most are laughing, but a few faces are fierce, hostile and sullen. Shouts of encouragement ring out. In an open space on the floor behind them, two ample women lie side by side with their skirts drawn up. They are on their backs and their shoes are off. Each has one hand around a bottle of beer and is holding one leg suspended in the air.

"One. Two. Three. Now, ladies, go!"

With the rhythm of the count, the women's opposing legs swing up from the floor, meet at the top of their arc and engage each other. There is a sound like hogs grunting.

"This is Louisiana leg-wrasslin'," shouts Big Lyle. "How you like it?"

"Take her, sweet Ruthie!" "Now, Nellie, now!"

Neat piles of five- and ten-dollar bills frame the heads of both women. They are in their forties and their fat is well muscled.

"They work in the shrimp factory," yells Big Lyle.

Just then, a wave of sound breaks from an adjoining room.

"A fight! It's a fight!"

The crowd pushes into a dark room with metal cones hanging from the ceiling reflecting light downward onto four pool tables. In one corner, two young men with pool cues face each other. The cues are raised like hockey sticks.

"You sumbitch. She's mine."

"You ain't even divorced. She's mine."

The men circle to the left and then to the right. The heavy end of one of the pool cues flies through the air and finds a collarbone. There is a sound like a twig snapping. Pain enters one man's face like a flicker of heat lightning. Both pool cues drop to the floor. One man turns and walks away. The other falls to his knees.

"Call a doctor! Call a doctor!"

Big Lyle steps behind me and pushes me forward. Thirty minutes later, after we've cleared the room, I've comforted the fallen and the police and ambulance have departed, I order my first drink. Dark rum. A triple. No water. No ice. Just neat, thank you very much.

Later that night, we take our seats beside the shortest man in the room, and Big Lyle introduces me to Trimmer. Trimmer works in a shipyard in Amelia. His specialty is repairing marine clutches. When he started working 12 years ago, Trimmer needed a heavy-duty tool to squeeze the clutch springs together, but over time he's developed the forearm muscles to do it by hand.

A big man wearing cutoff jeans moves in alongside us. His T-shirt says U.S. Naval Shipyard, Biloxi, Mississippi.

"They tell me you are pretty strong, little man," he says to Trimmer.

Trimmer smiles and looks down at his drink.

"I'm a black belt in karate," says Biloxi.

"I can't do karate," says Trimmer.

"What the hell can you do?"

Trimmer's hand darts out like a serpent's tongue, closes on Biloxi's arm just above the elbow and snaps shut like a vise-grip.

Biloxi stands up on his toes, puts his beer on the bar and closes his eyes.

"Do you mind if I drink your beer?" says Trimmer, still holding on.

"It's okay with me," says Biloxi. His voice is an octave higher.

Trimmer takes a long drink, puts the glass back down and releases his grip. Biloxi fades into the smoke and shadows.

❖

DC wakes often in the night, asking me twice for a cigarette. His sleep is restless; he wakes and then passes out again.

I wake up several times with a growing tightness in my knees and the unmerciful buzzing of a mosquito in my ear. Apparently unaffected by the pressure and lusting after the taste of human blood, it keeps power-diving across my face until I close my fist on it in mid-flight.

When I sleep, I dream of the Louisiana coast, a snake-infested maze of islands and split channels, hanging in the water, liberated from the earth. The air is sun-hazy and hot. There are no signs of human beings, but the waters below the surface are ferocious with life. The ocean of my dream is a smell, a swirl of water, a quality of light.

"You sayin' a Hail Mary for me?"

I lift my head, open my eyes and see DC staring at me. His eyes are bright and the color has returned to his face. He holds a paper cup of water in his hand; the pitcher beside him is half full.

"Bin drinkin', Doc, jus' like you told me."

I look at the pressure gauge. We are at 32 feet. The sun is streaming through the view ports. In a few minutes we will begin breathing pure oxygen. DC sees me staring at another cockroach walking across his silver flask.

"Don't worry, Doc, the bourbon's gone, but I've had enough to get me home."

FOURTEEN

SEPTEMBER 1968. I am lying flat on my back, my eyes closed and my stomach muscles on fire, thinking of inflicting some kind of mayhem on Dr. George Bond.

Six months ago, Bond asked me to meet him in Washington. When I entered his office at the Experimental Diving Unit, he closed the door and motioned me to sit in a hard-backed chair. He remained standing, his 6-foot-4-inch frame blocking out the light from the window.

"Still think you could do the job?"

"Yes, sir."

"You would be an outsider."

"I've always been an outsider."

"The Navy is tough on outsiders."

"I know that, sir. It's why I said yes when you first proposed the idea." Some months earlier, at a meeting of the Undersea Medical Society, I had presented a paper on our saturation dive at 630 feet. Shortly after, Bond had approached me and asked if I would be interested in assisting his medical team during *SeaLab 3*. The Navy was planning to place a station on the seafloor at 600 feet and five nine-man teams of aquanauts would occupy it for two months. *SeaLab 3* was going to be America's premiere seafloor colony.

"Have you any idea why I have asked you to come here?"

"To impart some good news—or bad news, sir."

"The bad news is that you went to the wrong medical school." He is smiling.

"I know that, sir. I went to the University of Toronto when I should have been at the school you went to, McGill University."

"I welcome the fact that you recognize the difference. The good news is that the Navy has finally approved your consulting contract."

He knew how much these words meant and gave me a few seconds to let them sink in. Five years ago, just before I started work with Ed Link, I received an official letter from the U.S. Navy saying that my application to join *SeaLab* had been turned down. The reasons given were that I was not a U.S. citizen, was not in the military and had no experience in diving medicine.

"To understand what our aquanauts are going through, I want you to train with them. You will attend their classes and dive with their equipment. If things go well, you might join one of the teams. I'd like you to report for duty at the San Francisco Naval Shipyard in September."

The shipyard is located at Hunter's Point on the west side of San Francisco Bay. The largest military yard on the west coast features the usual assortment of weathered docks, gray seawalls, rust-stained workshops and construction sheds. A line of warships and supply ships lies hard against its steel-and-concrete wharves.

On this scorcher of a morning, one week after my arrival, we have been exercising for more than fifty minutes and have just finished a third set of situps. Daily muscle-burning calisthenics followed by a two-mile run is a detail Bond had failed to describe in our conversation. I suspect he wanted me to discover it myself. He has succeeded; the fire raging through my stomach muscles is morphing into nausea.

"On your feet," barks the Navy drill instructor. "Give me 50 jumping jacks! Hup, one, two ..."

I struggle up, take a deep breath and begin making a series of half-hearted, arm-swinging movements. Sweat flies off my fingertips. I feel as if I have been time-warped back to Grade 12 phys ed with all its pain and humiliation.

The 45 *SeaLab* aquanauts in the gym are in the prime of life. The air around them reeks of sweat and male narcissism. They are hard-working, hard-drinking men filled with confidence, ambition and relentless optimism. Most of them are Navy men from bases in Florida and California.

Richard Blackburn and Berry Cannon are graduates of *SeaLab 2*. Bill Bunton is a diving supervisor at the U.S. Naval Undersea Warfare Center in southern California. Andy Pruna is an underwater photographer from the Naval Oceanographic Office in Washington. A Cuban exile, Pruna was almost killed by sniper fire during the invasion of the Bay of Pigs.

"Pick up the pace, you wing nuts. Pick it up!"

Two rows in front of me, a slim Navy commander is jumping higher than the instructor. Scott Carpenter used to be a college gymnast. Seven years ago, as a Navy pilot, he climbed inside the *Mercury 1* spacecraft and became the second American to orbit the earth. In 1964, he retired from the astronaut program to focus his attention on saturation diving and underwater engineering. As a team leader in *SeaLab 2,* Carpenter spent 30 days living at 205 feet. He's the first American to live in space and live under the sea. A few months ago, he was appointed Deputy On-Scene Commander of *SeaLab 3*.

The man in motion beside me has long black hair and a thick black beard. Philippe Cousteau has been diving since the age of four. In the 23 years since, he has spent hundreds of hours swimming at the side of his famous father as the elder Cousteau expanded his conquest of the depths.

"That's 50. Take a breather. Stand easy."

Directly in front me, the most accomplished saturation diver among us leans over to catch his breath. Bob Barth is a chief warrant officer from New London, Connecticut, whom I remember well from *SeaLab 1*. Since 1957, this veteran has devoted his blood, sweat and talent to the Navy's deep-diving program, spending more time in pressure chambers and undersea stations than anyone in the world.

Barth's muscular body is as straight as a gun barrel. I look up to see him wipe the sweat from his forehead and look in my direction. From our first conversation here in San Francisco, it is clear that Barth has serious doubts about men who do inexplicable things with their brains instead of obvious things with their hands.

We file slowly out of the gym and assemble on the asphalt roadway. There is no wind. Squadrons of gulls slant above the gray superstructure of an incoming destroyer. I make my way toward the end of the group of men and find myself standing next to Cousteau. He glances at me and bends down to tie his shoelace.

"All right," shouts the drill instructor, "let's move out."

Three abreast, we begin to jog along the roadway, heading toward the sun that hangs like a blood orange over the unruffled waters of San Francisco Bay. I am relieved to find myself in the second-last row, a convenient place to slow down without being too obvious.

The shipyard smells of fresh paint and diesel exhaust. We run toward the water and turn past a line of gray warships towering above the sluggish waters of the bay.

As we pass the building that houses our classrooms, a tall officer is standing in an open doorway looking at us. Bond is smoking his pipe and wearing his piano-key smile. If I had the strength, I'd give him the one-finger salute.

In truth, I feel apprehensive about this man with the shaggy eyebrows and engaging smile. He has the undying affection of dozens of men who admire him, even love him, for inventing saturation diving and making it possible for them to join him on his daring undersea odyssey. They know that when there are delays and accidents, Papa Topside uses his insight and humor to keep things on track. The problem is that Dr. George Bond is no longer in charge of his own program.

In the five years since I visited *SeaLab 1* and met Bond, the program has grown in size, cost and complexity. Instead of four men living at 193 feet, there will be 45 men in five teams living at 600 feet. Instead of a dozen undersea tasks, there are more than 30. The amount of life-support and work-support technology has tripled and the budget has jumped ten-fold to more than $10 million. Today there are more than 100 men, including the aquanauts, in the surface support team. In its wisdom, the Navy decided to make Bond the project's chief medical officer and turned the management of his program over to line officers with little first-hand experience in saturation diving. The result has been a series of numbing bureaucratic entanglements, mechanical problems and project postponements.

We jog along the paved area next to the quay, turn a corner, and pass a giant shipyard gantry and a racket of hammers, drills and welding torches. To our right is a sleek cruiser with yardmen in hard hats repairing her rocket launchers. On the other side is a large dry dock where gangs of welders and outfitters are working on *SeaLab 3*.

She is an enormous yellow cylinder 57 feet long and 12 feet in diameter. A short, round tower juts up from her top. Along her sides are 10 large view ports. She is trimmed with handrails and flanked with large gas cylinders. A steel cage encloses her bottom entry hatch to protect against sharks. Her interior holds a spacious laboratory and communications area, a well-appointed galley with a stove, refrigerator and freezer, and a sleeping area with 10 bunks.

SeaLab 3 is a modified version of *SeaLab 2*. Four years ago, when I first saw the unadorned architecture of *SeaLab 2*, I thought she looked squat and ugly. It was easy to believe she had been designed by a roomful of humorless admirals. In time, I came to realize that she was the product of an unscrupulously unsentimental engineering vision. Her beauty lay in an alignment of pipes, plates and portholes that reflect the precarious relationship between salt water and steel.

We turn and run across a square that opens up to the hazy, blue bay. Its distant shores and layered gleamings are a feast for the eye. Like all great bayous, its depths express physical laws as powerful as its surface beauty.

After we have run about a mile, lactic acid begins scorching the interior of my legs. I keep running because the men beside me radiate a raw animal vitality. They have been chosen for their intelligence, devotion to duty and unquestioning belief in the program. They carry me forward with the strength of their stride and the fierceness of their ambition.

Philippe Cousteau is running next to me. He is 6 foot 2 inches and built with loose-muscled dignity. His short stride and heavy breathing suggest that his legs might be seizing up. As I watch the sweat dripping off his nose, he winks and tosses his head with a motion that suggests we fall back together.

We step outside the column, let the last row of runners move ahead and then move in behind. We slow down and the column pulls away.

"My lungs are on fire," he says, panting.

"My legs are like jelly."

We struggle to catch our breath. Up ahead, the drill instructor exhorts the men to pick up the pace.

"That guy is the Marquis de Sade of muscular pain."

"When we get to the next corner," gasps Cousteau, "let's duck in behind that white building."

His suggestion is irresistible. When we reach the bend in the road, a dozen quick lateral steps carry us into the cool shade of the officer's quarters. We lean heavily against the white wooden planks. My legs feel like they are filled with lead shot.

"You're from Canada?"

I nod.

"I'm from Exhaustion, California."

We watch as a gray pickup truck drives slowly by. "Since we're both aliens," he says, "we should form the Alien Navy to fight the American obsession with physical torture."

"And their five-star obsession with bureaucracy," I add with a wheeze.

I can feel him studying me. "What do you mean?"

"This project has more management layers than a wedding cake. And it's a year behind schedule. I can't figure out what all these guys from Washington actually do."

He gazes out at the water and then at me. "This is not a project," he says wryly. "It's a testosterone battlefield."

Under the roof above us, a loudspeaker sputters to life and we hear the first, stirring bars of the American national anthem. Each morning, when the flag is raised at the shipyard, everyone comes to attention, turns to the nearest flag and listens to "The Star-Spangled Banner."

"Now's our chance." He points to a gap in the buildings that shows where the column has slowed to a halt.

We edge along in the shadows of two more buildings and wait until the last notes of the anthem have faded. Heads low, we sprint across the grass. When the column moves off, we are tucked away in its last row.

❖

I am alone in the diving locker trying to understand the intricacies of the Mark Eight diving helmet when I am frozen into stillness by a powerful voice behind me.

"Good afternoon, corporate doctor."

I always stop what I am doing when I hear George Bond's voice. It is deep and resonant, like an old motorcycle warming up. I turn to face him. A pipe hangs from his lower lip, ashes glowing brightly. It is rare to see Bond without his pipe. You can often smell his approach before you see him.

"How many of your body's 2,000 moving parts are in pain today?"

"All of them, sir."

"Does this mean that civilians can't take Navy training?"

"It does, sir. Civilians are used to feather beds and caviar. We are unaccustomed to breaking into a sweat before noon."

Bond has extravagant eyebrows, a broad nose, a thatch of white hair and cunning blue eyes.

"And what are you learning in your work with the Navy?" He looks at me as though inspecting something on a cotton swab.

"It has given me the desire to be a great doctor, not a great athlete. I am going to turn down my recent offer to play fullback for the Green Bay Packers."

"Wise decision. They will separate you from your shoulder blades as soon as you step on the field. You should remain in the locker room and read your books. What author has your current interest?"

"Conrad, sir. A man who, like yourself, is at home with the language of the foredeck."

"Given the pain on your face when you are running, I suspect you are reading *Heart of Darkness*."

Literacy is not a hallmark of Navy captains, but George Bond has a scriptural belief in the power of English prose.

"I am a disaster in running shoes, but I have a fatal attraction to books. *Lord Jim* is telling me how lack of courage changes a man's life."

U.S. Navy captain and physician Dr. George Bond, the "father" of saturation diving.
(Courtesy of Glen Loates)

Bond takes a long look around the room that houses the helmets, hoses and hot-water suits of his aquanauts. The wrinkles around his eyes are the lines of a man who thinks too much and faces an uncertain future.

Bond may not be the Navy's most effective manager, but he is a humane one. He knows the strengths and vulnerabilities of every one of his men. And he understands what they can and cannot do with their bodies and their recently developed diving machines. He is bold, but when his men's lives are at risk, he is as cautious as a grandmother.

"And just what do you think of the helmet you are holding in your smooth, uncallused civilian hand?"

"Well, sir, it worked fine in yesterday's pool dive and I'm sure it will deliver the goods during tomorrow's dive in the bay." I hold up the helmet. "But, as you can see, sir, it's as ugly as home-made sin."

Bond takes the pipe from his mouth and smiles. "It seems that you have learned one thing well."

"What's that, sir?"

"One of the most important things in a Navy diver's tool box is a rust-proof sense of humor."

"Thank you, sir."

"There's something else that will take you a lot longer to understand."

"What's that, sir?"

"A Navy diver has the toughest job a man can love."

❖

In the summer of 1965, I was invited by the U.S. Navy to visit *SeaLab 2* lying 205 feet off the coast of La Jolla, California. A short swim away was the upper edge of a submarine canyon. I spent three days on the Navy's support barge talking to Bond, the surface team and the divers, trying to understand the human dimensions of the project.

Each man had a personal version of what it was like to live under the Pacific Ocean for ten days.

"We had a problem leveling the station. The floor slanted so radically we called it the 'Tiltin' Hilton.'"

"The water was icy cold and depressingly dark. And there were times when clouds of sediment made it impossible for the divers to see more than a few feet."

"It was damn hard work. We were always cold and could never get enough sleep. There were times when we had difficulty breathing in the water. We got through by surfing on our adrenaline."

"Living inside the ocean, your senses and perceptions change. You forget about returning to the surface and become attuned to the depth of the station. You also become acutely aware of the abundance of sea life around you."

"It's easy to get disoriented in dark water. And if you put your hand on a scorpion fish, like Scott Carpenter did, its barb will puncture your skin and your arm will swell like a balloon. It's not fatal, but it's damned unpleasant, and you spend the next two days in bed trying to recover, cursing your bad luck."

One day, as we are sitting in a classroom, waiting for a lecture on sharks to begin, I overhear Bob Barth talking about his abiding respect for these superbly designed creatures. Barth grew up in South Africa where swimmers were sometimes pulled from crimson water missing an arm or a leg. "Big sharks, especially the great white, are eating machines," he says. "Thousand of pounds of teeth, jaws and skin—stretched over an appetite."

For the next hour, we listen to Professor Perry Gilbert, one of the world's foremost authorities, talk about the sleek predators at the apex of the ocean's food chain. Gilbert outlines the natural history of tiger sharks, bull sharks and the great white. He tells us that the great white shark grows to a maximum length of 21 feet and a maximum weight of about three tons. It can be identified by its massive size, black eyes, pointed snout and rows of serrated, triangular teeth. "Whitey" is the largest shark that preys on warm-blooded animals. It eats whales, dolphins, fish, squid and sometimes human beings. It is most commonly found in South Australia, South Africa and off the coast of California. Gilbert tells us that there is a possibility that one or more of these animals may be drawn to the activities around the station.

There is silence. Everyone in the room takes a measure of comfort in the steel cage that guards *SeaLab*'s entry hatch, but what would happen if a diver was out at the end of his breathing hose and cut his hand? He'd be a long way from the station, in the dark, with blood trailing off into the ocean; he'd be wondering when two rows of razor-sharp teeth would appear out of the darkness.

Two years ago, I spent 48 hours living in a small undersea station operated by Florida Atlantic University at the edge of the Gulf Stream. We were trying to see if a station placed in shallow water could be used for long-term, day-night study of coral reefs. On the second night, I was following a track back to the station when a 12-foot hammerhead swam into view and began swimming in circles around me. I was alone and far from the entry hatch. All I could see in the beam of my flashlight was muscle, silver belly, detached eyes and rows of inward-pointing teeth. This was her home and time had perfected her for it. As I watched, she made a sudden vertical thrust, bit the head off a passing amberjack, and disappeared.

"Dr. Gilbert," says someone in the front row, "*SeaLab* has equipment that will generate low-frequency noise at 600 feet. Do you think this noise will attract sharks or repel them?"

Perry Gilbert takes off his horn-rimmed glasses. "I don't know," he replies thoughtfully. "This is the first time that anyone has lived at 600 feet for two months. It's one of the things you'll find out during those 60 days."

⋅⟨⟩⋅

One night a week, Philippe Cousteau and I leave the shipyard in a rented car to explore the streets of San Francisco. Our first stop is usually North Beach, the old Italian neighborhood that was home to the Beat Generation and Jack Kerouac and Allen Ginsberg. Five years ago, the Beach became a bawdy strip of neon lights, loud music and go-go dancers shimmying in gold cages. It's a perfect place to have a drink and talk about life at Hunter's Point. We park the car just off Columbus Avenue and join the crowd at the Purple Onion or the Hungry i.

One night, during a pause in the music, Philippe puts his glass down and looks around the crowded room. I ask him why he is smiling.

"I like being in a place where no one cares that I am a Cousteau."

"Is it difficult being a Cousteau?"

"At times it is, because you are always dealing with other people's expectations."

Like Clay Link, Philippe appears to be a young man for whom the world has no boundaries. In fact, his situation is much more complicated.

"How do you cope with your father's fame?"

"I have learned how to do things beyond his reach. I fly airplanes. I've spent a month living in a station 300 feet below the surface of the sea. I'm thinking of making a feature film."

He waves his thin arm and a waiter turns and walks in our direction. Mindful of tomorrow's early morning run, we order our last drink.

"My father took the world's imagination into the ocean. I want to carry it into the sky."

We spend the next few minutes talking about the Apollo moon program. Sometime next year, three men are going to try to land on the surface of the moon.

"What about space? Would you like to journey into space with the astronauts?"

Cousteau looks at me with his father's enigmatic eyes. "As a species, we are creating more than enough problems on this side of the atmosphere. Maybe we should wait until we grow up before we fly into space."

"Stop talking like your old man. If they offered you a ride would you go?"

"*Dans un instant.*"

❖

With his long hair and black beard, Philippe could have been a poster boy for last year's Summer of Love in San Francisco. Because of our curiosity about what happened there, we make several trips into the

Haight-Ashbury district and walk the same streets where tens of thousands of young people inhaled incense, took drugs and listened to acid rock. Drawn by a romantic vision of social harmony, they jangled tambourines, got stoned and voiced their protest against the war in Vietnam.

As we stroll past the large Victorian-style houses with their Queen Anne towers and peer into bars and head shops, we see the familiar Indian headbands, army jackets, granny glasses and long dresses of the counter-culture. But in laneways and alleys we catch glimpses of drug pushers leaning over thin, shivering bodies wrapped in blankets.

"So much for Timothy Leary's better living through chemistry," says Cousteau.

In a coffee shop down the street from the Grateful Dead house, Cousteau tells me about his participation in *Conshelf Three*. The project cost $700,000 and involved 150 people. The station was built around an 18-foot sphere and was placed at a depth of 328 feet in the Mediterranean, seven miles west of Monaco.

"The sphere had two stories," says Philippe, "and rested on a chassis that held ballast tanks and cylinders of helium, oxygen and compressed air. In its upper story, six of us gathered data, talked to the surface and ate our meals. The lower story held sleeping, diving and sanitation facilities. We stayed down there for 27 days."

"How did you get to work?"

"We went out through a small bottom hatch open to the sea. Outside the hatch, just a breath-hold away, was a pair of decompression chambers. In an emergency, we knew we could climb into the chambers, close the hatches, get to the surface and be decompressed in big medical chambers."

During last week's dive into San Francisco Bay, Philippe had let it slip that he hated being cold. "What kind of gear did you wear in the 55-degree water?" I ask.

"We had thick neoprene suits and a vest of incompressible foam rubber. On our chests we wore two-way regulators that allowed high-pressure oxygen-helium to be pumped through hoses from the station. For safety, we carried a conventional three-tank aqualung filled with oxy-helium. We called it *le parachute*."

Like Stenuit and Lindbergh and the men of *SeaLab,* Philippe is a man who makes friends with his fear but does not talk about it. The look on his face confirms that it's not going to be part of this or any other conversation.

"What was the most important thing you did down there?"

"We had a series of maintenance tasks on a vertical stack of pipes and valves known in the oil business as a Christmas tree. After a few false starts, we finally worked out a technique that allowed us to repair them faster than on land. This is the kind of work that may pave the way for the permanent human occupation of the seafloor."

"What's it like to actually live—sleeping and swimming—for 27 days at 55 fathoms?"

In the long silence, I sense his mind returning to those implacable depths where he feels the ancient cold and sees faint slivers of light coming from the station's bottom hatch.

"Each time I swam away from the station," he says thoughtfully, "I was struck by one overpowering fact. I've lost the surface. It is far above me, out of sight, buried in the icy darkness. The surface means death. The bottom means safety. Our house inside the sea means light, warmth, friends—life itself."

We talk about the prolonged effect of cold and pressure. "Every one of those 27 days in the station was a constant test of ingenuity and determination. To survive, we solved more engineering problems in three weeks than in all our undersea operations since 1950."

He pauses, holding his coffee cup halfway to his lips. "One of the most frightening moments came when the suction pump that draws the diver's breathing gas back into the station stopped working, and then blew up. There was a strange rattling sound followed by an explosion. Pieces of hot metal bounced off the floor and the walls of the diving locker. We were damn lucky no one was hurt."

I look into his eyes. He is a member of a special guild that knows they have dues yet to pay.

"It took three and a half days to decompress from 328 feet. When it was over, I felt worse than I ever have. I was physically exhausted and mentally depleted. All my muscles ached. My mind felt like it was frozen. It was the hardest challenge of my life."

He is silent for a moment.

"The interior of the ocean is like nothing on earth. It wants everything. When you have nothing left, it wants twice as much again."

FIFTEEN

FEBRUARY 1969. The Hall of Gems at the Smithsonian Institution's National Museum of Natural History is a large, low-ceilinged room filled with display cases holding priceless collections of precious stones. Its centerpiece, gleaming behind a thick layer of bullet-proof glass, is the Hope diamond. This evening the Hall of Gems is the setting for an elegant black-tie dinner.

The tuxedo I rented this morning in downtown Washington is riding high under my armpits, threatening to shut off the circulation to my fingers. The circular table in front of me is covered with crystal glasses and plates groaning with food. The tables next to us are filled with smiling people in long gowns and freshly pressed shirts. Jon Lindbergh and Ed Link seem to be enjoying the three-course dinner, but I have left mine untouched.

"You okay?" asks Ed Link.

"Yes, sir, everything's under control."

I am lying. Six months ago, Jon Lindbergh and I agreed to deliver the 1969 Link Foundation lecture. When dinner is over, I am going to have to go down the hall to the Smithsonian theater, where I will stand up in front of hundreds of scientists, politicians and company presidents. I am terrified that I am going to forget or fumble my words. For the second time in less than an hour, I excuse myself from the table and head for the washroom.

There is another reason for wishing I was somewhere else. After months of postponements, *SeaLab 3* is being lowered to the bottom off the coast of California today. I was hoping to be with the medical support team when the first aquanauts took up residence at 600 feet.

Two months ago, *SeaLab 3* was lifted onto a 2,000-ton construction barge and towed out to San Clemente Island, 70 miles northwest of San Diego. The low, undulating hills of the Navy-owned island are used for long-range gunnery practice. In the deep water off its shores, submerged nuclear submarines test-fire Polaris and Poseidon missiles. *SeaLab* and her support ship, the USS *Elk River*, are in Wilson Cove, a protected bay off the island's north end.

I have invested months with my colleagues on the medical team getting ready for the initial descent. Our workplace is on the 230-foot-long *Elk River*, a former rocket launching ship with wide, gray decks that contain a world of nautical machinery. Her main feature is a central "moon pool" that gives protected access to the ocean. Next to the moon pool are two 12-ton diving bells and a pair of 24-foot-long decompression chambers. Each chamber has a large living area and five berths.

To descend to *SeaLab,* a team of five men will be compressed to 600 feet in one of the chambers. After reaching this depth, they will climb up through a mating collar into their diving bell. The bell will be unlocked from the chamber and a gantry will lower it through the moon pool to the seafloor 600 feet below. When the divers arrive on the bottom they will open the lower hatch, put on their breathing equipment and swim the short distance to *SeaLab*. After their 12-day mission, they will ride back to the surface in the diving bell and be decompressed in the chambers.

Mounted on the *Elk River*'s main deck are two all-white, one-story structures—the command and medical vans. The command van has a row of windows and workstations with headsets and television monitors. The medical van has a similar row of workstations with pressure gauges and gas analyzers to monitor the percentage of oxygen-helium inside *SeaLab* and the bells and chambers. In addition, its shelves and drawers contain the instruments and equipment of a working hospital.

For the past month, the *Elk River* has been a boomtown on the water, its decks and workshops filled with swarms of officers, contractors, subcontractors, sailors and divers struggling to complete the final installation and testing of the hundreds of systems and subsystems needed to make *SeaLab* function. Scattered among them were reporters and cameramen from major newspapers and television networks.

The American press has become enchanted with the adventure of living in outer space and under the sea. In less than six months, three astronauts are going to attempt the first landing on the moon. In less than a day, 45 men in rotating teams are going to inhabit a station on the outer edge of the California continental shelf. Deep ocean dives are exciting to cover, especially when there is a live television feed from 100 fathoms.

For the Pentagon, a riveting undersea story is a welcome diversion from the depressing news about the war in Southeast Asia. *SeaLab* has become a shrine to the U.S. Navy's undersea capabilities, confirmation that if America isn't winning in Vietnam, it is at least leading the race to place outposts on the floor of the ocean.

I return to the dinner table, but my mind keeps drifting out to the Pacific Ocean and the men who have devoted the best years of their lives to the *SeaLab* project. They are more dedicated to the success of their program than any group of men I have ever met. They have worked tirelessly to bring the project this far. However, to a man, they are apprehensive about the project's state of readiness.

One of their major concerns is their diving equipment. The Navy's Mark Eight and Mark Nine breathing units require constant monitoring and their thick hoses are awkward to handle. The units have been tested in shallow water, but not at 600 feet. The same is true of the neoprene suits designed to keep a constant layer of hot water next to the diver's skin. Their heaters, pumps and hoses have never been tested at 600 feet.

Another concern is that, instead of medical officers, line officers are managing the project. Line officers are good men, but unfamiliar with the psychological and physiological stresses of saturation diving. Most of them have never dealt with a full-blown medical emergency. Although the Navy calls *SeaLab 3* an ocean engineering project, it is really an experiment in undersea medicine and human performance at an extreme depth.

Two days ago in our living quarters on San Clemente, Philippe Cousteau told me that he had become increasingly uneasy about months of delays followed by a frantic scramble to launch *SeaLab* on its most recently announced date.

"A group of sleep-deprived officers," he said, "is being forced to choose between another postponement and ignoring the risks. They have decided to ignore the risks."

"What would you do?"

"My father taught me that when you are testing a new, unknown life-support system against the ocean, you don't allow a schedule to interfere."

One of the great strengths of Navy divers is their seafaring professionalism. They are capable, patriotic men willing to put their lives on the line for little more than being able to say they did it. However, for most of them, the dives to 600 feet have been reduced to a simple technical challenge with so many last-minute problems that thinking about things is unimportant. Now is time for action; thinking comes later.

At precisely eight o'clock, Jon Lindbergh and I walk up to the stage of the 500-seat auditorium and adjust our notes on the lectern. My legs are weak, but the rehearsals and the pressure not to screw up are carrying me forward. The title of our talk is "Underwater Man—His Evolution and Explorations." I take a deep breath and begin.

"Today's underwater man, with his new diving systems and submarines, is nothing more than an extension of the ancient terrestrial human who first yearned for unlimited time and depth mobility beneath the sea," I say. "Let us imagine that we are standing on a unique underwater seamount from which we can glimpse the past, present and future."

For the next hour, Jon and I take the audience on a historical tour of the struggle to dive, work and eventually live inside the ocean. We start with the early explorations of Aristotle in the Mediterranean and move quickly to the sixteenth century.

"Among the devices was an inverted wooden barrel built by De Lorena in 1531. The barrel fit over his head and shoulders. Utilizing air stored in flasks, he was able to remain underwater for over an hour," explains Jon. "A significant improvement was made by Edmond Halley, the astronomer, who, in 1690, conceived a diving bell that held 60 cubic feet of air, had clear glass at the top to let in light and a rudimentary valve for ventilation ..."

While he speaks, I gaze out at the faces of the people in the front rows. They are senior executives from the National Geographic Society, the Smithsonian Institution, the Singer Corporation, General Precision and Union Carbide. Their eyes are fixed on the large screen in the center of the stage showing old line drawings of men crouched inside the crude wooden devices.

After describing the hand-cranked submarine designed by David Bushnell in 1776 and the critical medical research conducted by French scientist Paul Bert, we bring the audience into the twentieth century.

"As underwater man approached the mid-twentieth century, the United States Navy began investigating the use of a helium oxygen mixture as a substitute for air."

Jon, a member of the Naval Reserve and the officer-in-charge of many salvage operations, describes one of his early helium dives.

With helium diving, I quickly learned the problems of in-water decompression. On my first working dive to 260 feet, my weight belt of about 60 pounds fell off. I quickly grabbed it, because without it I would surface out of control and possibly die. As there was still some work to be done, I hobbled around the bottom clinging to this weight belt. At the 50-foot stop on the way back up there was a twinge in my elbows that I thought was an ache from hanging on to the belt. At 40 feet, which was the last stop before the surface, the lead seemed to be getting much heavier. On the surface, there was no longer any question; both elbows began to throb with a deep boring pain. The tenders seemed to take hours in getting my helmet off and aiming me toward the decompression chamber.

Because the French have made such unique contributions to living under the sea, I describe my recent visit to observe the work being done by Jacques Cousteau and his team.

"Just two months ago, I traveled to Marseille, France, to see an experiment where goats, which are used as experimental diving animals, were successfully exposed to depths of over half a mile. At 3,280 feet, the goats appeared normal. Although we cannot extrapolate from goats to men, it is likely that helium will be a passport for some very deep diving."

I notice Ed Link sitting in the front row between his wife, Marion, and his sister, Marilyn. He is a man at the top of his game, surrounded by his family, friends and admirers. He is working on the engineering design for a new research sub called the *Johnson-Sea-Link*. He and his friend Seward Johnson, sitting a few seats away, are planning to build a research facility called Harbor Branch Oceanographic on the east coast of Florida.

Like Cousteau, Link arrived at this time in history with sea-changing ideas. His greatest asset is to be an inventor with the imagination and will to leverage his inventions, and the teams that make them useful, into successful commercial enterprises.

Cousteau is a world traveler, a raconteur whose greatest asset is to understand that people are eager for dramatic stories from inside the ocean. Through his books and films, he speaks directly to a wide audience, defining issues, if not answers, in an enduring way.

Jon's final words contain a prophecy that will take years to happen and decades to be revealed.

The seas are vast, and fixed stations cannot hope to provide access to more than a minute part of the area we need to study. Lockout subs combine the range of the submarine with the versatility of the diver. If we follow Mr. Link's concept in logical sequence, we will install high-pressure living quarters with a lockout capability into an ocean-going nuclear submarine ... if the future of underwater man looks bright and unlimited, it is because of the efforts of many men. Foremost among them is a gentleman Joe and I have had the privilege of working with for several years. We are speaking of course of Edwin Link, who has spent his life with his eyes and mind on the future.

After the lecture, I wind down with a few drinks with old friends in the bar at the Mayflower Hotel. I am so relieved to be off the stage that I have more than my share of rum.

Later that night, the phone rings in my hotel room. I can't find the light and fumble around in the dark. My head hurts. Finally, I get the phone up to my ear.

It is Philippe Cousteau. He waits until I am fully awake before he comes to the point.

"There's been an accident," he says quietly. "Berry Cannon has been killed. He was at 600 feet, trying to open the hatch. No one knows why it happened."

SIXTEEN

I LIE AWAKE FOR HOURS, staring at the shadows on the ceiling and listening to the traffic in the street outside my window. The next morning, in the hotel newsstand, I read the front-page headlines of *The New York Times,* the *Los Angeles Times* and the *Chicago Tribune,* and a cold sweat glues my shirt to my back.

> Veteran Aquanaut Dies During Deep Dive on *SeaLab* Project
> Aquanaut Dies in Dive 600 Feet Down, Test Halted
> Diver Dies; Suspend Test

I pick up a copy of the *Washington Post,* find an empty table in the coffee shop and read the page-one story.

> *SeaLab* Test Halted after Diver Dies
>
> The Navy suspended its *SeaLab 3* experiment yesterday after veteran aquanaut Berry L. Cannon died diving in frigid Pacific waters 610 feet below the surface. The first aquanaut to die since the *SeaLab* project began operations almost five years ago, Cannon suffered a seizure of some kind two minutes after leaving a diving bell just above the ocean floor off California's San Clemente Island early yesterday morning.
>
> The story described how Bob Barth pulled Cannon back to the diving bell and how Barth and his teammates gave him heart massage and

mechanical resuscitation while the bell was being pulled up to the USS *Elk River*. The following paragraphs said that 33-year-old Cannon was pronounced dead in the *Elk River's* decompression chamber and that his death might have been due to a number of reasons including "cardiac failure." According to the text, the Navy was suspending diving operations until the reason for the fatality was clarified.

The last paragraph quoted a Navy spokesman as saying, "We don't know what happened to Cannon, though we are certain it was not equipment failure."

Cannon was an electronics engineer at the Navy's Mine Defense Laboratory in Panama City, Florida, and one of the most accomplished divers on the team. During *SeaLab 2,* he spent 15 days living at 205 feet.

He was one of those quiet men who manage to telegraph their feelings simply by the way they turn their heads and listen. On my first day in San Francisco, as I was putting my diving gear away in a locker, he saw that I was alone and asked if there was anything he could do to help me in my new surroundings. "This is a tough bunch of sailors," he said, "but if you take care of them, they'll take care of you."

As he spoke, he looked directly at me. Behind his handsome, deep-set eyes and his shy smile were a seaman's self-reliance and a deep sense of duty to the men on the project.

❖

A day later, I climb back on board the *Elk River* and head across the main deck to the medical van. It is filled with men sitting silently in front of their control consoles, looking at depth gauges, gas analyzers and closed-circuit television screens. Some of them are writing in notebooks. Others are staring straight ahead. The air around them is charged.

Two Navy doctors, Paul Lineaweaver and Mark Bradley, are directing the decompression of the team that went to the bottom with Cannon. They ask me to participate in the round-the-clock watch-keeping chores. During the next 24 hours, I discover what happened to Berry Cannon.

On February 16th, at 11:00 P.M., *SeaLab* was lowered to a depth of 610 feet. Soon after, the surface team discovered that oxygen-helium was leaking from its interior. Early the next morning, the loss of gas increased and the first team of aquanauts were ordered to dive. Cannon, Bob Barth, Richard Blackburn and John Reeves climbed into one decompression chamber and were compressed to 610 feet in three hours. The other five members of Team One were compressed to the same depth in the second chamber.

The first diving bell reached the bottom at 6:00 P.M. on the 17th. With Blackburn and Reeves remaining inside, Barth and Cannon swam over to the entry hatch, a distance of about 25 feet. Their job was to open the hatch, get inside and repair the leak. The water temperature was a bitter 48 degrees Fahrenheit. Both men were wearing single-layer neoprene wet suits and Mark Nine breathing units with separate face masks and mouthpieces.

Within 10 minutes both men returned to the diving bell shivering violently. Because of the over-pressure inside *SeaLab,* Barth was unable to lift the entry hatch. The bell was brought back up to the *Elk River* and mated to its decompression chamber. Still at 610 feet of pressure, the men transferred into the chamber to warm up and get some rest.

Early in the morning of the 18th, the gas loss increased substantially and there was concern that the interior of *SeaLab,* with all its instruments and equipment, might flood. At 5:00 A.M., Barth, Cannon, Reeves and Blackburn were ordered to go back down. Once again, the diving bell landed about 25 feet from the station. Barth and Cannon dropped out of the bell and swam over to the entry hatch.

In the command van, I watch the videotape of what happened next. Barth is standing on the ladder under the entry hatch. He tries to lift the hatch, but does not succeed. He swims to his right to get a crowbar out of a tool rack. He returns to the ladder, looks over to his left and sees Cannon lying on his back. Cannon's face mask is off and his mouthpiece has fallen out of his mouth. Barth attempts to revive Cannon with Cannon's spare mouthpiece. Then Barth begins dragging Cannon toward the diving bell. As both men move off the screen to the left, it looks like Cannon is having a seizure.

I step outside the van. The sky is filled with gray haze and the ship is rolling on the long swells passing under her keel. Indifferent to any human emotion, their size and weight are unassailable.

As the decompression continues, the senior officers spend hours behind closed doors, discussing the accident and what they plan to do next. When they step into the medical van, the look on their faces says: "We're trying hard to process this and understand the full meaning of what has happened."

The closed-circuit television monitors give us a close-up view of the eight decompressing divers. One chamber holds Barth, Blackburn and Reeves. The second holds the other five men. Each is coping with sadness and confusion.

Our hearts go out to all of them, especially Barth. He is the team leader. He and Cannon were selected for the task because they had more experience than anyone else. Berry Cannon was his close friend. Barth made the second dive knowing that he and Cannon were being asked to do something that flew in the face of every caution instilled in them since they started diving. Keep warm. Breathe easy. Don't hurry.

In his book *Sea Dwellers,* Barth describes what happened. "Our plan for the initial dive was to make a normal slow descent to 610 feet ... there are nine men in Team One. I elected to take four down to get the station open and running. Then I would call for the other five guys. Suddenly this plan seemed inadequate ... our house was sitting down there losing more gas than we have to spare."

The thick bundle of hoses and cables that carried electrical power, communication and video feeds from the surface to the station was leaking oxygen-helium at a rate of 3,000 cubic feet an hour. Most of the gas was streaming out through the area where the cables penetrated *SeaLab's* hull. The gas had to be replaced or the station would flood. Estimates indicated that the oxygen-helium supply on the *Elk River* would last for less than a day.

Every time Barth and his teammates strapped on their breathing gear to go deep, they sensed—but didn't necessarily believe—that an accident might happen. All they knew for certain is that they had been working

16-hour days for the past five months to get this far. It didn't matter that the hot-water suits weren't ready or their breathing systems hadn't been tested at 600 feet. The only thing that mattered was that everyone was counting on them to solve a critical problem. Getting down to the bottom and opening up the station was something that had to be done, right now. Barth writes:

> There were a lot of concerned folks topside trying to work on solutions to save the station ... we decided to get the first four people in the deck chamber, make a rapid descent to depth and then transfer to the bell to make the actual trip to the bottom ... a lot was going on topside. Their concern continued to mount as they witnessed the loss of gas.
>
> Our trip to the bottom was not the fastest bell run we ever made and the bell was without heat. By the time we got down and opened the hatch, all four of us were colder than hell. However, we had a lot to do and were in a hurry, which kept us from thinking too much about the cold. Getting out of the bell and into the station was our primary goal.

When Barth and Cannon reached the bottom they were shivering uncontrollably. Within seconds of stepping down into the 48-degree ocean—as cold as a glass of ice water—their heart rates and breathing rates shot up and their muscles began to stiffen. Their one-layer wet suits offered little protection; they were well into the first phase of hypothermia.

The two men paused for a few seconds just outside the bell, their eyes adjusting to a night without starlight. Then they pushed off, concentrating on making their rigid muscles move them toward the big yellow station. They were gasping for breath. To satisfy their respiratory needs they switched on the emergency bypass of their Mark Nines. Barth's description continues:

> The procedure to get inside was not a simple one ... we had about 15 minutes of work outside before we could attempt to open the

hatch. Berry and I had trained for this event and knew what had
to be done. Our first job was to exit the bell, make our way to the
station and commence the unbuttoning procedure. This called for
flooding a large ballast tank, shutting and opening a few valves,
swimming from one end of the house to the other to make sure it is
level, then using some of the existing pressure inside to blow down
the entrance-way skirt. This done, we were to open the hatch, get
in there, seal the leaks ... then I would have the other two divers
come over ...

The counter-balanced entry hatch had a deadweight of 150 pounds,
and Barth used a crowbar to try to lift it. Unfortunately, the men in the
command van had over-pressurized the station's interior. Unknown to
Barth, he was trying to lift a hatch that weighed more than five tons.

As I struggled to open the hatch, Berry was close at hand doing
what he was supposed to do. For some frustrating reason I couldn't
get the hatch open and couldn't figure out why ... with the equipment we were using, there were no communications with the other
diver. ... As we were extremely cold and tiring rapidly, Berry and I
headed back to the bell. A good deal of our problem was due to the
cold. Without warm water and nothing on but a wet suit, it didn't
take long before the cold made us lethargic.

The swim from the bell and the work on the station added dramatically to their hypothermia. They were fighting for each breath and
moving with uncoordinated movements. Their ability to think clearly
had melted away. Cannon was the first to arrive back to the bell.
According to Blackburn, "he was dazed and incoherent." Barth was in
the same condition. Both men needed help from their teammates to
climb up into the bell.

As the four divers were brought up to the ship and transferred to the
deck chamber, oxygen-helium continued to leak through a burst sheath-
ing in the main electrical cable. The loss rate climbed to 15,000 cubic feet

an hour. In about four hours, when the backup supply ran out, the station would flood. The reporters and photographers waiting on San Clemente had been assured that the dive would begin the next day. Ignoring the fact that simply wanting to make a dive at a certain time does not overcome the imperatives of nature, the officers in charge of the project decided to press on.

Although they had now been awake for 20 hours, Barth and Cannon were assigned the task of a second attempt. They were given amphetamine pills to take if they needed them. To keep them warm on their next dive, hot-water hoses were rigged to the outside of the bell. After they dropped outside the bell, Barth and Cannon would connect the hoses to the hot-water suits. The Navy-designed full-face mask did not provide a satisfactory seal when used with the Mark Nine system, so, as in the first dive, both men would use a standard face mask and mouthpiece. As Barth tells it,

> When our shivering slowed down, we had a brief conference with the topside folks to figure out what we needed to do next. The clock was still ticking and we didn't have time to waste. Earlier, we sent out through the air lock our semi-closed diving rigs that we wore on our first trip to the bottom. In exchange, they sent us two new rigs along with the hot-water suits.
>
> Inside the bell we disconnected from the decompression chamber and started down for trip number two. I remember sitting next to Berry, both of us huddled under a big blanket trying to retain what little heat we had ... I don't ever remember being that cold. Finally, after what felt like an eternity, we were on the bottom again. We opened the hatch, reached out for that wonderful hot-water hose, brought it inside and in complete horror looked at a small trickle of water that was the temperature of a drinking fountain.
>
> Hot-water suits are loose fitting and require a good deal of hot water to work properly. Without that water they aren't a hell of a lot of comfort at 610 feet. Accepting the fact that we wouldn't have hot

water to warm our suits, we elected to go without it, hoping for the best.

Berry and I each grabbed a new diving rig, put it on and went outside. … When the cold seawater ran down the back of my neck it felt warm … the water outside, at a mere 48° F, also gave the strange impression of being warm.

Berry and I met outside the bell for a brief moment getting our hoses ready for the short trip to the station. As we floated there, Berry tapped me on the shoulder and pointed in the direction of the station … I was glad we took this moment. What we saw … was this magnificent big yellow dwelling resting comfortably on the bottom. There were many lights and they were all on. Berry and I could see various outcroppings on the seabed around our future home. It was a magnificent sight. Here we were at just over 600 feet swimming around in the Pacific Ocean. To top it off, we were going to be staying down here for two whole weeks.

In the bell we left two divers, John Reeves and Dick Blackburn, who would wait there until it was time for them to come over. In the second decompression chamber topside, there were five other members of Team One awaiting their call to the seabed. Four other teams up there were working and waiting for their stay in this home. Berry and I were preparing to be the first two guys inside to start the adventure. It was a day we had been thinking about for a long, long time.

During these brief seconds of reflection, floating over a seafloor made flat by millions of years of water, Barth and Cannon were beyond the limit of their physical capabilities. Cold and fatigue had rendered them incapable of recognizing onrushing threats.

Berry and I made our way over to the station and started, for the second time, the procedure to get inside. I was still trying to figure out why I couldn't get the damn hatch open and Berry had a couple of things left to do. I swam over to get the crowbar. I was determined to get the damn hatch open this time. With my back to Berry, who was not far away, I got the crowbar from its holder. I heard Berry in the background. My impression of this noise was that Berry was working and probably grunting. When I turned around, I saw Berry in convulsions, thrashing around on the seabed, with his face mask at his side.

In the flash of awareness that such moments bring, Barth feels like the first—or last—person on earth. Something is suffocating Cannon's brain cells, costing him huge amounts of air hunger and pain.

I dropped the crowbar and swam over to Berry. Pulling him over to the area under the hatch, I tried to get him breathing again. His mouthpiece was no longer in his mouth so I grabbed the buddy-breathing regulator and tried to get it in his mouth. I tried again and again, but his convulsions had forced his mouth shut. The whole process wasn't working and I knew I was wasting valuable time.

I grabbed Berry and started swimming back to the bell with him. The bell looked like it was a million miles away. His umbilical hose or mine kept hanging up on something or other and I had to stop and free it. Berry's convulsions dwindled down to no movement at all. I knew then without a doubt I had just lost my friend.

Dragging Berry inside we got him started on CPR and made the bell ready for the lift back to the surface ... we kept falling into the water while working on Berry ... the folks in the topside control room must have been going crazy ... we were trying to get a mouthpiece into Berry in the hope we might get him breathing again ... I glanced at the internal bell pressure gauge and it read well over 800 feet ... all this gas we were trying to get into Berry was driving us deeper ... I reached over and vented the bell back to 610 feet and hoped no one had noticed.

As they worked on Cannon, the men inside the bell clenched their teeth and smothered their groans. Death had entered the bell and was occupying the spaces between them.

> On the way back to the surface I said, "Berry Cannon is dead." It seemed like the most logical thing to say. These words must have broken everyone's heart up there ... for a brief moment inside that goddamn bell, the three of us looked down at our dead comrade knowing that we were also looking at the end of the *SeaLab* program.

In the breaks between my watch-standing duties, I walk slowly around the ship. The men in the command van have faces as rigid as sheet steel. Some of them gaze at the video screens as if wishing for the power to rewind what they have just seen and start all over again. When they signed on for this Navy project, there was no indication that they would get caught up in something like this. No one warned them that when a man dives on the deep edge of the continental shelf the difference between life and death is the merest chance, or that if a man's luck allows him to escape once, the odds are much shorter the second time.

All of us on board the *Elk River* are part of a new generation of explorers who have staked our careers on undersea technology. The technology is novel; our challenge and responsibility are to prove it will work in an ancient and unpredictable ocean. Then, in a fierce fusion of physics and physiology, Berry Cannon is killed. All of a sudden, we lose confidence in the technology, and a few of us begin to wonder at what point a long, deep dive into the ocean turned into an incremental descent into impaired judgment.

❖

Eleven days after the accident, a small group of men wearing naval uniforms and carrying heavy briefcases walks through the front doors of the Naval Undersea Warfare Center at Point Loma in San Diego. In a quiet, air-conditioned room, *SeaLab* officers, aquanauts and a panel of invited experts begin giving sworn testimonies to the Naval Board of Inquiry. Chaired by Captain John Chase, Commander of the Naval Weapons Facility at Dahlgren, Virginia, the inquiry remains in session for 12 days. It is closed to the press and public.

Dr. Robert Creason, San Diego's county coroner, states that Cannon's death was caused by respiratory failure due to carbon dioxide poisoning. Dr. F. Luibel, a San Diego pathologist, says that this opinion is predicated on an analysis of an air sample taken many hours after the accident. Based on the pathology findings alone, he says, the exact cause of death cannot be determined.

Lieutenant Commander Larry Raymond, an aquanaut from Bethesda Naval Hospital and an expert on thermal stress, tells the inquiry that Cannon lost a considerable amount of body heat during both dives. Due to the pressure, which is 19 times that on the surface, he says, Cannon's neoprene wet suit was only a fraction of its normal thickness and offered no effective insulation against the 48-degree water. Because he was wearing neither gloves nor hood, Cannon's hands and head were directly exposed to the cold. According to Raymond, Barth and Cannon probably started their second dive with their core temperatures below normal. The combination of fatigue, breathing cold gas and a drop in core temperature could have initiated a lethal increase in heart rate called cardiac arrhythmia.

As the inquiry proceeds, there are moments when the men in the room drift away from the subject they have been asked to ascertain—the cause of Berry Cannon's death. There is a tense description of the installation of the wrong-sized neoprene sleeves that led to the critical loss of helium from the station. There are heated accusations that someone tampered with an emergency breathing system oxygen valve outside one of the decompression chambers. Some questions reveal that only a few aquanauts had used their breathing units at depths greater than 60 feet.

At one point, Bob Barth stands up, squares his shoulders and tells the inquiry: "I wasn't getting enough oxygen. It was like trying to work while holding your breath."

Richard Blackburn, whose muscular arms lifted both Barth and Cannon back into the bell, chooses his words with great care. "We were all pushed to the point where mistakes were inevitable … our training looked good on paper, but that was all … the work was too hard, too long … with no consideration for what the divers must contend with … my teammates felt tired, overworked … the dive should never have been made …"

Toward the end of the inquiry, the lengthy questions and answers orbit around one indisputable fact. The Mark Nine breathing unit used by Berry Cannon had a canister that was supposed to contain a carbon dioxide–absorbing chemical. For some reason, the canister was empty. Cannon didn't have a chance. He was hyperventilating from the cold. His exhaled carbon dioxide rose rapidly and became toxic. According to Dr. Robert Workman of the Naval Medical Research Institute, even at sea level, a diver breathing through a Mark Nine unit with an empty canister would be in serious trouble in less than 60 seconds.

How could this have happened? Chief Petty Officer Paul A. Wells, described by other witnesses as beyond reproach in his honesty and work habits, tells the inquiry that he believed the units were "ready to go" the day Cannon died. He says that he would have noticed if the canisters were empty by their weight. A full canister, he says, weighs about eight pounds and accounts for about 17 percent of the weight of the Mark Nine.

It might be argued that the lack of chemical absorbent was not the primary cause of Berry Cannon's death; it was more like the final blow. He and Barth and the others began their first dive already severely stressed from overwork and fatigue. They used a breathing unit and diving suit that were technically inadequate and untested. They should not have made the second dive. It's a miracle that Barth wasn't killed, too.

Whatever the physical cause of the accident, it is clear that the decision-making culture played a crucial role. The Navy saw the success achieved by Bond and his associates in *SeaLab 1* and *SeaLab 2,* and decided that bigger was better. The men they picked to manage *SeaLab 3* had never worked with so many layers of complex equipment, demanding physics and over-stressed physiologies. These were men who did everything they could with the information they had available. They had all the right people, asked all the right questions, considered all the right factors, and then came up with the wrong answers. In spite of the best intentions, *SeaLab* became a program that contained the seeds of its own destruction.

Fatigue impairs judgment and performance. Cold can interfere with the rhythm of the heart. Lack of chemical absorbent in a canister can cause convulsions. However, each of these events is only part of the story, and is perhaps not even the most important part.

We will never know if Berry Cannon's death was due to a single, indecipherable error or a sustained series of mistakes and malfunctions. We do know that, faced with an assignment of surrealistic absurdity, he fought until his lungs ached and his mouth filled with the taste of copper.

In some ways, all of us working on the *Elk River* during those final weeks were to blame for Berry Cannon's death. We sensed the risks, but thought we could finesse our way around them. We were wrong.

SEVENTEEN

JULY 1969. It's a small, freshwater bay and its curved limestone shoreline is well protected from the big fall storms that blow in from the northwest. It's uninhabited except for a single cottage surrounded by thick groves of pine and cedar. The only sounds are shore birds and waves breaking against its rocky beach. As soon as I saw its unusually clear water, I knew it would make a perfect location for *Sublimnos,* Canada's first underwater station.

Just beyond the green arms of the bay is Lake Huron, one of the five Great Lakes, part of an enormous freshwater sea shared by Canada and the United States. The Great Lakes hold 10 percent of North America's liquid fresh water and cover 95,000 square miles. Thirty million people, many of them living in cities such as Chicago, Detroit, Cleveland and Toronto, are within a day's drive of their shores.

"Ready?" I say to the neoprene-suited diver standing in the water beside me.

"Sure, let's go."

Doug Elsey is one of the young volunteers helping me with the *Sublimnos* project. A few months ago, he showed up at a lecture I was giving in Toronto and asked if we could talk for a few minutes. He told me he was 23 years old, lived in Thunder Bay, Ontario, and was studying ocean engineering at Florida Atlantic University. He had read about my work with Ed Link in *National Geographic.*

"I hear that you are going to put a small station in the Great Lakes."

"Some time in the middle of June."

"Is there any way I might join your team?"

"We're working on a shoestring, so I am not sure I'll be able to pay you."

Elsey shifted his weight from one foot to the other. "Money's not the most important thing. I'm going to be an ocean engineer. I've read about undersea stations and I want to find out how they work."

"This is a pretty modest station."

"It's the only one in Canada."

I invited him to make the three-hour drive from Toronto to the site.

"Let's see if you and the project are meant for each other," I said. "And if you are, then we'll figure out a way to reimburse you."

Elsey arrived three days ago with his dive gear and a ready sense of humor. Today he's already spent 10 hours hauling equipment from the dive shed down to the shoreline and out to the station. His self-deprecating wisecracks have made the work much easier for all of us. In addition, he's spent more time underwater than any member of the team.

"Short, stubby guys like me who can put their brains into neutral are made for this kind of work," he says with a wry smile.

It is dusk and a full moon is rising out of the big lake beyond the mouth of the bay. There is one last dive to make, so we put on our face masks and fins and push off from the limestone ledge that marks the shoreline.

In the months following the cancellation of *SeaLab 3*, I began to think about how I might make a contribution to the concept of living in the sea. All the stations I had worked on were complex and costly. Perhaps there was a place for a small, inexpensive structure easy to operate and accessible to large numbers of divers.

I applied for a $15,000 research grant from the National Geographic Society and asked Steve Selwyn, an engineer in New York, to help me with the design and construction. Starting with a steel cylinder used for shipping liquids on railway cars, we cut and welded a vertical, air-filled compartment—9 feet high and 8 feet in diameter—that holds four people. Access to its interior is through a 35-inch hatch in the floor. Inside, there is a circular bench and fold-down table. A small, transparent dome on the top of the station and four side windows provide 11 square feet of viewing area. There is no room to sleep, but space enough for people to look out the windows and see the great waters from a new perspective. One of our divers says it's an "underwater classroom." Another calls it "Canada's first underwater think tank."

Dr. Alan Emery, a marine biologist at the Royal Ontario Museum in Toronto, helped me find the site at the tip of the Bruce Peninsula. He's going to use concrete cinder blocks to build an artificial reef next to the station and observe the animals and plants that take up residence. As well, he and his team will conduct extensive fish surveys in the bay. When winter comes, we will continue our work by cutting a hole in the ice and diving down to the station to test hot-water suits and new breathing units.

I decided to call the station *Sublimnos,* a combination of Latin and Greek meaning "under fresh water." A week ago, its living compartment was lowered into the bay and attached to a similar-sized compartment containing 10 tons of iron ballast. This evening, Elsey and I are going down to hook up the underwater telephone.

Even in the twilight water, it is easy to find the station. We follow a staircase of elephant-gray rock into the depths and then head east across the floor of the bay—a horizontal distance of about 130 feet.

The rocks beneath our fins were formed 400 million years ago, in Silurian times, as coral reefs and lime mud at the bottom of a warm sea. Time, water and ice have transformed them into pitted slabs separated by cracks and fissures. Today they are part of an ancient system of cliffs called the Niagara Escarpment, best known for where the mighty river cascades over Niagara Falls. To see the Falls is to wonder about that ancient ocean and the unfinished processes that continue to make them what they are.

The bay is located on the northeastern shore of a long peninsula that separates Lake Huron from Georgian Bay. The nearby depths hold more than 25 known shipwrecks. Most of them are side-wheelers, steam barges and sailing ships that went to the bottom in the nineteenth century during fierce autumn storms.

Just shy of six feet tall, Elsey pushes his fins through the water with a powerful leg kick. In his black neoprene wet suit, he looks like a chunky leopard seal.

"I spent a few years as a commercial diver," he told me when we first met, "but I wanted something more challenging. That's why I picked ocean engineering."

"Any idea how you are going to apply it?"

"Not yet. All I know is that I want to work under the ocean with people whose eyes are on the future."

We reach the bottom of the bay and head across the sediments in an easterly direction. Even with a spare tank of air cradled in his arms, Elsey has no trouble keeping up.

The water that holds us is as cold as the sea off San Clemente Island, a reminder of the time 12,000 years ago when the great glaciers crept out of the Arctic and this part of the world was covered with mile-high ice. I am thankful for the thick wet suit that covers everything except my face.

The water in front of my face mask swarms with invisible, microscopic life, including bacteria, ciliates and phytoplankton. During the afternoon dive we saw several species of fish, including cisco and bottom-dwelling sculpin. But tonight all we see is a flat stretch of sediment and lengthening shadows.

Elsey stops swimming, tucks the air tank under one arm and unsnaps a flashlight from his weight belt. He switches it on and a golden cone of light spreads across the lakebed. A few seconds later, the light bores through the emptiness and finds the yellow-painted ballast compartment.

With a series of confident moves, Elsey swims under the entrance hatch, takes off his scuba gear and places it carefully on top of the ballast compartment. When he is safely inside I begin a slow circular swim to see what *Sublimnos* looks like at this time of night.

From the bottom of its ballast compartment to the top of its view dome, the station is 16 feet high. Four steel channel beams hold the living compartment three feet above the ballast. Even in the darkness, there is enough moonlight streaming through the water to show the gold and blue stripes painted on the living compartment.

Through one of the windows, I see Elsey bent over the table working on the telephone. He has placed the wide-beam flashlight on the bench beside him so that it points at the ceiling and bathes his hands and face in a soft orange light.

After I have made a complete circle, I swim over the top of the station and peer through its transparent dome. Its smoothly curved surface makes the interior of the station look smaller, as if seen through the wrong end of a telescope.

I swim away from the station until the light coming from its windows is barely visible in the darkness. This project is a turning point in my career. It's the first time I've been totally responsible for a serious under-water activity; I've had to raise every dollar, design a meaningful program and find a small group of divers like Elsey who want to make it work. I have little social life; during the past year, I've spent every weekend and dozens of days stolen from my other work to get the station into the water. And, if anything goes wrong and someone gets hurt, I could face a battery of lawyers and lawsuits. Fortunately, it's a challenge that comes at a time when there are fewer demands for my skills as a diving physician.

Most of the living-in-the-sea objectives for science and salvage estab-lished by the U.S. Navy in 1964 have been achieved. As well, Berry Cannon's death and the high operational costs of these undersea programs have sent French and American ocean engineers looking for other ways to work safely at continental shelf depths. One technology being developed is undersea robots; another is a pressure-protecting suit. Either option means improved diver safety and less need for a physician.

Something else is on my mind. In the years since I began working underwater, great changes have occurred in the oceans and lakes of the world. Over-fishing and pollution are altering the chemistry and life of the world's biggest ecosystem. In ways we do not understand, these factors may be affecting the health of the human family.

In the year-long struggle to get this project under way, I asked myself why anyone should care about a small bay on a big lake 200 miles north of Toronto. After all, the lake is only one of millions in the world. But I had to start somewhere. And since we began working here, the character of the lake—its fusion of color and light—has gone into me. I've discov-ered that the lake is more than my natural heritage; it is my responsibility.

•:•:•

In the months to come, more than 2,000 men and women, some of them from 10 Canadian and American universities, will join us in the quest to understand the dynamic ecology of this bay. We will learn many things about the animals and plants that dwell here. We will cold-water test 50 different diving devices, including closed-circuit breathing systems and underwater cameras. To our surprise, we will discover that the real significance of *Sublimnos* is not engineering or science. It is how the time spent here changes our attitudes and perceptions about this part of the planet by allowing us to think hard about what it means to be here. Our aqualungs and wet suits and the station give us the capability to look deep into these waters and consider our role in their future.

•:•:•

I shrug out of my scuba harness, hang it on a steel peg outside the station and duck under the entrance hatch. With water streaming off my head and shoulders, I pull myself up on the bench beside Elsey.

"I was beginning to think you'd been swallowed by the great freshwater night-shark," he says with a grin.

"Just taking a look around."

"Now that you're in here, it's time for another blast of fresh air."

"Is that a physiological requirement or a reference to something else?"

Elsey laughs, picks up the scuba tank and gives its valve a couple of turns. There is a sharp hissing sound.

"I've wired up the phone and tried to call the guys on shore, but there's no answer. Maybe they've stepped outside the shed. Let's give them a couple of minutes and try again."

Elsey turns out the light and our eyes slowly adjust to the darkness.

"So, now that you've had a chance to see this project from the inside," I ask, "what would you like to do?"

"I'd like to work with you, as an engineer."

"Have you any idea what the challenges are?"

"This is a non-profit venture. Everyone has a full-time job, so they only work on weekends and vacations. Which means they work twice as hard."

"And what are your personal objectives in all this?"

"*Sublimnos* is a one-room schoolhouse. I'm going to learn as much as I can, as quick as I can."

Elsey looks up at the dome-shaped view port in the ceiling. "I've seen my share of strange things, but I've never seen anything like that." His last words trail off in a whisper.

I shift along the bench to get a better view. In the center of the circular dome is the full moon with liquid, quivering edges.

"It's amazing to think that in a few days, three guys in bulky white suits are going to step out of a spacecraft and walk on its surface."

"If they make it, it's going to be the most remembered event of our lifetime."

We watch in silence as a thin strand of cloud brushes the face of the moon and then disappears into the watery darkness.

Later, after we have made contact with the shore team and are getting ready to leave the station, Elsey asks me what I am planning to do after *Sublimnos.*

"I'd like to build the first completely transparent undersea station to give divers a panoramic view of the ocean."

"Where would you use it?"

"I'd field-test it here and if it works and we can find the money, use it in the Arctic Ocean."

"Why the Arctic?"

"It's the least-known part of Canada and our largest marine ecosystem. To really understand it, we're going to have to learn how to work safely under the six-foot-thick ice that covers it for most of the year."

Elsey smiles. "I thought that Toronto was the least-known part of Canada." Then he looks at me hard. "Do you have a name for it?"

"I'm thinking of calling it *Sub Igloo.*"

Since our first conversation, Elsey has reminded me of what it is like to be young, ambitious and in search of meaningful work. He laughingly describes himself as a "solid C student," but he's much more than that. He is a hard worker with a sense of humor who knows that one of his greatest assets is his tireless enthusiasm. And he also knows that if he is going to work in a new frontier, he has to make himself rapidly indispensable.

"If you give me sketches of the sphere and how you want to ballast it, I could turn them into a set of engineering drawings."

"When would you start work on it?"

"Tomorrow."

EIGHTEEN

JULY 1969. The Florida night is hot and still, the air scented with sea grass and salt. Across 3,000 yards of black marsh and low scrub, an immense white rocket is suspended in floodlights. Three hundred and sixty feet from base to tip—six stories higher than the Statue of Liberty—the Apollo Saturn is being loaded with liquid oxygen and super-cold fuel. When full, it will weigh six million pounds and contain as much explosive power as an atomic bomb. The beams of light fanning through the haze reflect off the rocket onto the surface of a saltwater lagoon.

I have come to observe the launch of the first spacecraft designed to land men on the moon because it is the boldest fusion of science and technology ever attempted. I am also interested in the similarities between ocean and space exploration. Astronauts spend hundreds of hours under water learning to adapt to the weightlessness they encounter orbiting the earth. Space is a proving ground for some of the life-support technologies we use under the sea.

Diving medicine and space medicine have many things in common. Both are concerned with weightlessness, isolation and confinement. Both focus on the physiology and control of breathing gases and how to minimize the risks of sudden decompression. An advance in one field almost always has an application in the other.

Two months ago, I applied to the *Toronto Telegram* for a press pass for the launch of *Apollo 11*. In exchange, I agreed to write an article about the mission.

An hour ago, I climbed aboard a bus with a sweating mob of reporters and cameramen for a pre-launch look at the Apollo Saturn rocket. After a 30-minute drive over a long, blacktop road past two security stations, the bus rolled to a stop, and we stepped out into the sweltering summer heat. As the photographers set up their tripods, I walked ahead of the bus, keeping to the side of the road until I was alone.

The brilliantly lit rocket, looking more like a skyscraper than a spaceship, stands next to its dark red gantry, its cryogenic tanks spewing plumes of vapor into the darkness. The gantry is taller than the rocket and has service arms attached to critical sections of its exterior. In seven hours, Neil Armstrong, Buzz Aldrin and Mike Collins will walk across the highest arm of the gantry and slide carefully into the command module. Each will settle into his couch, hook up his oxygen hose and plug in his communication line. After brief handshakes and wordless farewells, the hatch will be closed and the final phase of the countdown will begin.

In the silence and heat of the night, the luminous form of the Apollo Saturn is a reminder that we are new to the universe and should have a sense of wonder about everything. Six years of working under the sea has taught me that meaningful exploration, the kind that leads to wisdom, begins with a reverence for the primal mystery of the unknown.

A few hours later, the sun rises out of the Atlantic Ocean behind the launch pad. As we watch from the press site three and a half miles away, the Apollo Saturn sits like a spike in the clear blue sky. A thin, cryogenic cloud wreaths its upper stages.

There are more than a thousand reporters, television journalists and photographers sitting in the grandstand or standing on the short-cropped grass in front of the radio and television trailers. They are drinking coffee and talking in low voices. Occasionally, they stop and look over at the sky-pointing structure in the distance.

After a short burst of static, a carefully modulated voice booms from the row of black loudspeakers in front of us:

This is Apollo Saturn launch control. T minus 61 minutes and counting. T minus 61 minutes on the *Apollo 11* countdown, and all elements are GO at this time. Astronaut Neil Armstrong has just completed a series of checks on that big service propulsion system engine that sits below him in the stack.

The oceans are crucial to this first-ever attempt to put men on the moon. The rocket will be launched over the Atlantic because, if it explodes, its fiery pieces will fall into open water. When the command module returns to Earth, it will land in the Pacific, where there is plenty of room for an overshoot.

I line up at a trailer for coffee and then walk across the grass through clusters of reporters and hundreds of still and television cameras. At the edge of a lagoon, I find a short reach of sand and sit down. In front of me is tranquil dark water stretching toward a broad tidal marsh. Even here, I can still hear the loudspeaker.

Coming up shortly will be a key test here in the firing room. It's some final checks of the destruct system aboard the three stages of the *Saturn V* launch vehicle. In the event during powered flight that the vehicle strays violently off course, the range safety officer can take action to destroy the vehicle.

The tidal marsh in front of me is part of a National Wildlife Preserve and home to hundreds of species of birds, mammals and amphibians. The preserve and nearby waters teem with manatees, dolphins and alligators. Between the press site and the rocket is a waist-high pampas of cord grass, snake cotton and needle rush growing out of thin layers of mud and Holocene sand. Inside its thick hatch is an empire of spiders, grasshoppers and butterflies. Like all wetlands, this is a nursery for the sea and the land, a place where things begin.

We're 5 minutes, 20 seconds and counting … the spacecraft test conductor for the lunar module reported that Eagle is GO. The swing arm is now coming back to its fully retracted position as our countdown continues …

We are GO for *Apollo 11*. We'll go on an automatic sequence at three minutes and seven seconds.

I focus my binoculars on the rocket. The climbing sun renders it ivory and makes the black bars and vertical letters painted on its side clearly visible. I see a blur, move the binoculars and pick up a small white bird descending on the far side of the lagoon. A royal tern with a scarlet beak lands on the black spotted muck between the roots of a small mangrove tree. The water in front of it is all shadows and glint.

Two minutes, 10 seconds and counting. The target for the *Apollo 11* astronauts, the moon. At liftoff we'll be at a distance of 218,096 miles ... we're approaching the 60-second mark ... Neil Armstrong just reported back, "It's been a real smooth countdown." ... Forty seconds away from the *Apollo 11* liftoff. All the second stage tanks now pressurized. Thirty-five seconds and counting. We are still GO with *Apollo 11*. Thirty seconds and counting. Astronauts reported, "feels good." T minus 25 seconds ... T minus 15 seconds, guidance is internal, 12, 11, 10, 9, ignition sequence starts, six, five, four, three, two, one, zero, all engines running. Liftoff. We have liftoff, 32 minutes past the hour. Liftoff on *Apollo 11*.

The last few words are barely audible. Ten seconds before liftoff, jets of fire burst from the base of the rocket. Flames sluice downward into two huge concrete channels, ram into enormous heat sinks of water and boil up into orange-white clouds of steam on both sides of the launch platform. The thrust is twice the power of all the rivers and streams of North America channeled through turbines.

The rocket begins to rise a full six seconds before the roar of its engines reaches our ears. Because of the distance, it looks like it is silently levitating on a pillar of fire.

The sound comes in waves, first a hard crackling like the snapping of twigs, then a furious, ear-splitting explosion that grows louder and louder until the ground quivers and shakes.

Apollo Saturn slowly rises until it clears the towering gantry. The pillar of fire lengthens until it is longer than the rocket. People in the crowd are clapping and cheering. The rocket climbs through a thin layer of cloud, slants to the southeast, and goes up and over the ocean. After a minute, all that is visible are thin white flames shooting from its base.

Inside the fading thunder are three men who will spend the next 66 hours crossing the gulf between the earth and the moon. In less than three days, they will look out a triangular window and see a strange and deserted landscape of mountains, canyons and craters. Then, while one of them orbits in the command module, the other two will descend to the surface of the moon in the lunar excursion module, climb into their pressurized space suits, back out though a narrow hatch, descend nine rungs of a ladder, and step off into moon dust.

The rock-covered surface in front of them will range in color from light tan to ashen gray. There will be no sign of water. The pronounced curve of the horizon will confirm they are standing on a celestial body roughly a quarter the size of the earth. Because it has no atmosphere, the sky will be utterly black. The centerpiece of the heavens will be a radiant blue sphere small enough to hide behind an astronaut's outstretched, gloved thumb.

But now, at this point, the Apollo Saturn rocket hones off to a white point so fine it has nearly vanished. In the marshland, the cicadas are resuming their shrill. I sweep my binoculars slowly across the lagoon. The royal tern has disappeared. A few feet out from the shoreline, a line of bubbles rises to the surface. The bubbles shine briefly in the sunlight, burst, and then disappear.

NINETEEN

AUGUST 1970. "How deep do you think we might go?" he asks. He is smiling, his magnetic blue eyes shining in a face still wet from the 100-foot scuba dive we have just completed. Behind him, the Caribbean Sea shimmers with heat and possibilities. I look across at the brawny Royal Canadian Mounted Police officer assigned to guard him during this short vacation in Belize. Three days ago, the officer made it clear that one of the reasons I am on this trip is to safeguard the life of the prime minister while he is diving. "Let me think about it," I say.

Pierre Trudeau is slim, muscular and 49 years old. An accomplished scuba diver, he's the first Canadian prime minister to explore all three dimensions of the lakes, rivers and oceans of Canada. He has surfed big Pacific waves off British Columbia and taken month-long canoe trips down rivers flowing into the Arctic Ocean. He does these things not because he is bold, but because he is curious.

A few hours later, after he finishes studying his government briefing books, I make a suggestion. "Let's go a little deeper each day, say 50 feet, and see how deep we get." He agrees, and the next day we dive to 150 feet. Trudeau is an efficient swimmer, using just the right muscles to propel himself downward with effortless grace. On the way back up, he stops to look at a cluster of black coral attached to the vertical wall beside us. I can sense him wondering about the underwater realm of our planet, so remote from his work as a statesman, yet so connected to the wilderness he loves.

On our last day, we swim down across a vast slope of sand and over the edge of a cliff. I glance at my depth gauge. We are at 180 feet. As we descend through 200 feet, a large spotted grouper stares at us, turns, and glides under a rocky overhang into a small cave. There is no sound except the rattle of exhaust air escaping from our breathing regulators. The intermittent cascade of bubbles spilling out of his regulator confirms that he is breathing slowly, conserving his air.

I stop at 250 feet and he eases in beside me, our shoulders almost touching, his fins working the water to maintain an even depth. He looks around, savoring the mystery of a place he is seeing for the first time. On one side is a sea-cliff that continues downward to a depth of 600 feet. On the other side are shades of blue and purple rising out of an impenetrable blackness.

I feel the rapture of nitrogen narcosis flooding my brain and am certain he does too. There is no time to waste. I unfold a small Canadian flag, shake his hand and present it to him. The first head of state to swim this deep into the ocean has a mile-wide grin on his face. In less than a minute, we are on our way back to the surface, following the silver trail of our exhaust bubbles up toward the sunlight.

On the flight back to Canada, he asks me about diving research in the United States, and I tell him about some of the new undersea technologies being used to bring the ocean's resources, especially oil and gas, up to the surface. In the future, these technologies will affect the development of offshore oil and gas fields in Canadian waters. He listens quietly, sometimes glancing out the window at the passing clouds. "Applied science produces real miracles," he says quietly, "but on land, technology and unrestrained growth are having devastating consequences. If the *Torrey Canyon* oil spill is any indication, I suspect the same is true of the ocean."

I look out the window at the cloud-stitched horizon. Three years ago, the 120,000-ton supertanker *Torrey Canyon* was stranded on a reef off the British coast. Over the next few days, 35 million gallons of crude oozed from her hull and headed toward the beaches of Cornwall and Brittany. A desperate British government sent jet aircraft to bomb the wreck and burn off the remaining oil. Flames and smoke rose hundreds of feet into the air. Tens of thousands of seabirds suffocated in the wave-tossed oil.

The world's first major oil spill was caused by a ship's captain who took a shortcut because he wanted to dock before the next low tide.

❖

It is six months after our trip to Belize and the prime minister of Canada and I are sitting on the edge of a work barge in Greater Lameshur Bay in the U.S. Virgin Islands. It is August, and a fierce Caribbean sun burns down from an orange-white sky. Beneath the stretch of blue water in front of us is the most ambitious undersea-living experiment ever undertaken.

Tektite 2 is a $5-million program funded by the United States government and a partnership of corporations and universities. Over a period of seven months, 53 scientists, in five-person teams, are spending as long as a month in a large, four-room station at a depth of 50 feet.

Tektite 2 has a dual mission. It is a long-term study of the ocean and preparation for distant journeys in space. Most of its participants are marine scientists, but one of them is a NASA human-factors engineer working on the design and efficiency of space stations. Everyone inside *Tektite* is eating the same food as the *Apollo* astronauts. In addition, they are under constant television scrutiny by the NASA psychologists who are responsible for planning future space missions.

The *Tektite* scientists spend as much as 10 hours a day in the water. Geologists are studying the dynamics of seafloor sediments. Biologists are observing the behavior of tropical fish communities and the vulnerability of coral reefs to human activities. Together they are pooling their fragments of hard-won information into an understanding of life on the Lameshur Bay reef and the great ocean beyond.

Sitting quietly in his sun-bleached swimming trunks and swim fins, Pierre Trudeau studies everything going on around him. A few steps away, his RCMP bodyguard stands with his arms crossed and sweat dripping off his forehead. In a few minutes, the man whose life he is responsible for is going to disappear under the sea.

Trudeau extends his arms upward and a young man in khaki shorts lifts a large, rectangular breathing unit onto his back and tightens its shoulder straps. Trudeau looks into the young man's eyes. "It's pretty heavy," he says. "I don't think I'd like to haul it over a two-mile portage."

The 50-pound device is the most advanced undersea breathing unit ever built. Under its white fiberglass cover are control and delivery components similar to those used by the *Apollo* astronauts. With each breath, oxygen is added and carbon dioxide removed. There are no exhaust bubbles. However, if its electronic heart fails, an unsuspecting diver could quickly lose consciousness.

This morning, when we arrived at *Tektite 2*'s shore facility on St. John's Island, Dr. Jim Miller, the U.S. Navy psychologist in charge of the program, asked if we'd like to try the Mark One system. Without hesitation, the master of three languages with a brown belt in judo said, "Sure, why not?"

"Ready?" I ask.

"Let's take a look at what the Americans are doing."

I slide into the water, turn and face him. Pressing his fins flat on the water to steady his entry, Trudeau drops in beside me. Two safety divers, both wearing conventional scuba equipment, move into position beside us. We exhale and begin to descend.

Our heads are barely below the surface of the sunlit water when we see the station positioned on a stretch of sand next to a pale escarpment of coral. Its two circular steel towers, rising out of a large rectangular base, give it a stark, industrial look. A patina of green algae speckles its white paint. Air and water hoses and an electrical cable run from its base across the sand toward the shore, 200 yards away.

Beneath us, two members of the resident research team glide over the reef, heading toward the station. Sighting something, they change direction and descend toward a crevice that cuts into the edge of the coral. A pair of spiny lobsters is moving backward, crawling out of the living stone onto the bright sand plateau.

Like the animals they are studying, the scientists are 24-hour residents of the ocean, their existence linked to the ebb and flow of undersea life. They have seen sunsets through a rippling distance of water and watched the water-swirled lightning of tropical storms passing high overhead. An earlier team has experienced the velvet rumble of an undersea earthquake. For everyone living inside *Tektite,* the ocean has turned into something intimate and wondrously ungraspable.

Our first stop is the observation cupola, a circle of 10 rectangular windows on top of one of the towers. Each window emits a shaft of faint yellow light. As we drift around the perimeter, I slow my breathing. For the first time, I am inside the ocean inhaling and exhaling from a closed-circuit breathing device that leaves no upward spiral of noisy bubbles. The near-silence allows me to hear the muted clicks and whistles of unseen creatures.

The prime minister briefly closes his eyes. It seems that the man who spends most of his days in the corridors of power is not just looking at the ocean; he is coexisting with it, letting it inform him.

As we circle the cupola, Trudeau puts his fingertips on the lower edge of one of the rectangular windows and draws himself closer to look down into the room below. While his eyes study what is in front of him, he breathes from deep inside his chest, as if doing a yoga exercise.

We swim the short distance to the second tower, descend to one of its large, domed view ports, and look into the station's main control room. It is 9 feet high and 12 feet in diameter. The racks and shelves on its curved walls hold gas analyzers, pressure gauges, technical manuals and television monitors. On its far side are a second view port and a short tunnel leading to the other tower. The floor of the room is covered in wall-to-wall carpeting.

Tektite 2 is the Cadillac of undersea stations. The three adjoining rooms contain a well-equipped lab, five bunks, a heat-and-serve galley, a stereo system and a freshwater shower. A central air conditioner maintains the atmosphere—9 percent oxygen in 91 percent nitrogen—at a comfortable and relatively dry 80 degrees Fahrenheit.

This is the tenth mission in the seven-month program. On the far side of the control room a young engineer sits at a desk writing in a notebook. An arm's-length away, under the window, two scuba units stand ready for emergency use.

One of the participants in this mission is Bates Littlehales, the *National Geographic* photographer who, six years ago, recorded our long,

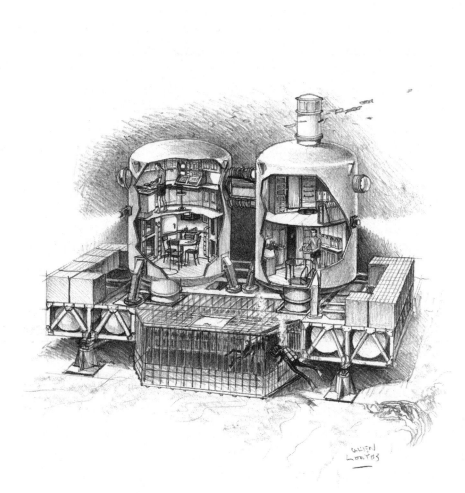

Tektite 2 undersea station on the bottom of Lameshur Bay. *(Courtesy of Glen Loates)*

deep dive in the Bahamas. Bates is somewhere in the water behind us, taking pictures of the prime minister's visit.

With his fins moving back and forth effortlessly, one of the world's youngest heads of state peers through the hemispheric view port. He leans forward, scanning the contents of the control room, as if trying to understand the real meaning of the multimillion-dollar station, its scientists and their research projects.

Trudeau has always been fascinated with technology. He wants to know how it works and how it integrates with the natural world. He wants to understand the relationships between technology, living creatures and the human community—and how they might be more mutually beneficial.

There is a practical edge to his curiosity. He has heard American oil companies discuss plans for deepwater drilling off the Canadian coast. He has seen the American government claim that Canada's Northwest Passage is an international strait. During the past two summers, a mammoth oil tanker, the USS *Manhattan,* smashed its way through the ice-covered passage from the Atlantic to the Pacific. Trudeau believes that drilling for oil and then transporting millions of gallons of it out of the new fields north of Alaska could harm the health of the polar ocean.

The voyage of the *Manhattan* and the *Torrey Canyon* oil spill have prompted his government to make Arctic environmental protection a priority. They are studying the implications of a new law called the *Arctic Waters Pollution Prevention Act.*

Pierre Trudeau does not have the engineering know-how of Ed Link or the environmental proficiency of Jacques Cousteau. But he believes that people are connected to each other, responsible for one another and capable of figuring out how to fix seemingly insolvable problems.

Canada has the world's longest coastline and almost a million square miles of continental shelf, most of it in the Arctic. A few days ago, Trudeau told me that his government is starting to work on Canada's first national ocean policy. "To give the policy real meaning," he said, "we need people who know the inside of the ocean. Perhaps you'd be willing to lend us a hand."

I told him I would give him an answer before we returned to Canada.

I have serious reservations about working for the government in Ottawa. I'm uncomfortable in meeting rooms debating abstract policy issues. I'm not good at writing long, arcane memorandums. On the other hand, I want to make a contribution to the country that has given me so much. The more I think about it, the more my decision is influenced by my admiration for a man who doesn't hesitate to use an unfamiliar breathing system or make a dive to 250 feet. Inspired by his daring deeds and intellect, I say yes.

As we head back to the surface, I take a last, long look at the station. It is sitting in a place where sunlight and shadows converge in reflective, liquid planes. Like the ocean that surrounds it, it seems to be saying, "Come and find out."

TWENTY

DECEMBER 1972. I am 600 miles north of the Arctic Circle, swimming under the six-foot-thick ice of Canada's Northwest Passage. The water is as clear as Steuben glass. When a filigree of frost begins to form inside my face mask, I lean forward, lift the skirt of the mask, and let a trickle of seawater clear my lens. The frigid brine burns painfully across my skin.

Ahead, in the light fringing the work area, an eight-foot Plexiglas dome rotates slowly on its barely visible lift lines. As the men standing on the ice over my head slack those lines, the dome begins a curved descent toward the seafloor—a slow-motion movement that suggests the touchdown of a ghostly spaceship.

A diver gives the dome a gentle shove toward an aluminum ring supported by 16 struts attached to a circular ballast tray. Beneath the ring, another plastic hemisphere, partner to the dome, is already in place. I am looking at *Sub Igloo,* about to become the first manned dive station in the polar oceans.

In the cone of light beneath the pack ice overhead, Phil Nuytten struggles to join the two hemispheres in a watertight fit. The water that suspends him is a sub-freezing 28.5 degrees Fahrenheit. It is so cold it feels like boiling acid. If you were not wearing a diving suit, it would paralyze your muscles, force you to gasp for breath, and accelerate your heart rate to lethal levels. If you are unprotected in water this cold, you better get out of the ocean fast, or there's a good chance you'll be on intimate terms with your own mortality.

We are in Resolute Bay on Cornwallis Island, about 125 miles from

the north magnetic pole. We are so far north that a week ago I stood on
the ice outside our tent and saw the northern lights in the southern sky.

We have come here with Canadian government support to help
unlock the secrets of a huge, ice-choked realm—the polar continental
shelf. In Canada alone, it covers almost a million square miles and yet,
because of its remoteness, human eyes have seen less than a few city
blocks' worth.

In two previous expeditions to this bay, we discovered how little
was known about arctic marine life, underwater ice structures and the
composition of the seafloor. We also discovered how little we knew
about surviving in one of Earth's most inhospitable environments.

We are working inside an ocean that for most of the year has no
waves, ripples or swells. Its primary surface is a layer of rock-hard ice. And
when winds shift or temperatures drop, the ice cracks and shifts, making
sounds like gunshots. There are stories of polar ice splitting open without
warning and spilling an entire camp into the sea.

The world of darkness above the ice is equally daunting. At this time
of year, the sun is invisible, the temperature plummets to minus 45 degrees
Fahrenheit, and winds seem to tear the skin off your face. While we were
putting up the dive tent, the wind gusted up to 35 miles an hour—a wind-
chill factor of 80 degrees below zero.

It has taken me two long years to organize this expedition. It began
when I moved to Ottawa to join the team of gray-suited bureaucrats
writing the national ocean policy. As the policy took shape and it became
clear that Arctic sovereignty was a key issue, I saw an opportunity to make
my dream of exploring the northern waters a reality. "If Canada's polar
sovereignty is to have any real meaning," I said, "we'll need to have a presence on the seabed." I proposed a series of four undersea expeditions—
one for each season of the year—to confirm Canada's capability to work
under the ice on its polar continental shelf.

This is my third expedition. It has been a long, interlocking chain of
meetings in Ottawa, Department of National Defence aircraft, tracked
vehicles, snow machines, tents, stoves, fuel drums, hundreds of crates and
containers of diving equipment, and a team of talented, tenacious men.

There are 15 of them here—scientists, technicians and engineers with hard, salty grins—and they can make things and fix things even when their fingers are frozen.

For the next month, our primary purpose is to clarify the challenges of scientific diving under the ice and evaluate the diving equipment we think will allow us to do it safely. As well, we are analyzing human performance. When we finish, we will have made more than 200 dives, studied cold-water suits, helmets and breathing gear, and learned how much work a skilled diver can attempt in these waters.

As I swim toward *Sub Igloo*, I hear a voice through an underwater speaker. It is Birger Anderson, our topside supervisor.

"Once the dome is in place over the hemisphere, give us two tugs on the line and we'll give you some slack."

I duck my head into the air bubble of a nearby *Sea Shell*, a clear acrylic communication booth, pull my mouthpiece forward, and speak slowly into a microphone. "OK, Birger. Phil is just centering the two hemispheres at the equator. I'll let you know when we're ready."

Anderson is a psychologist from California who studies human performance in high-risk environments. He is sitting in front of a small table in a tent on the ice above us. I can picture him with a clipboard in one hand and a microphone in the other. "The Arctic is a place outside the limits of my experience," he told me when he stepped off the plane in Resolute Bay. He looked across the runway into the sub-freezing cold and darkness. "It's challenges like this that make us bold and decisive, and show us exactly who we are."

"When you two are free," he says through the speaker, "I'd like you to return to the dive hole for a body-temperature check."

"OK, as soon as we're free."

Yesterday I swallowed an electronic pill designed to measure the temperature deep inside my body and send out a continuous radio signal. But the cold has weakened its batteries, so I must return to the surface to have my core temperature read directly. Even a small temperature drop means my body is becoming hypothermic and I will have to get out of the water immediately.

It's time to give Nuytten a hand. I duck below the rim of the *Sea Shell*, push off and "moon walk" across the seafloor toward *Sub Igloo*. We have discovered that wearing swim fins near the bottom creates large plumes of sediment that reduce visibility to zero, so I remove my fins and carefully dance forward like an Apollo astronaut heading toward the Lunar Excursion Module. Later in the expedition, Scott Carpenter, my old friend from *SeaLab 3*, will join us for a few days and take this same "weightless" walk over the seabed.

As I near *Sub Igloo*, a small jellyfish with a glowing skirt drifts into the light. In the summer of 1970, when I brought my first expedition to Resolute Bay, I was astonished by the vast numbers of animals and plants living in the water column and sea bottom. The ice itself, which did not seem a likely place for life to thrive, was riddled with brine channels in which single-celled algae flourished year-round. There were cracks and crevices where larger creatures such as ctenophores and amphipods had taken up temporary residence. We called them "the ice lovers."

I reach *Sub Igloo* and begin to work beside Nuytten, fastening the bolts that clamp the domes together. We have been underwater for almost an hour, and my hands feel like frozen hamburger. I try to work smoothly, but with my body encased in an inflatable neoprene suit and my fingers swaddled in foam rubber, it's like trying to drive a car with your elbows.

The daunting cold sharpens our perceptions of other risks. One is that when *Sub Igloo* is filled with air, it will become a giant bubble straining toward the surface with an upward force of eight tons. To keep it from breaking free and smashing against the ice, we have placed eight and a half tons of ballast in the trays beneath the struts.

We try not to swim over the top of *Sub Igloo*. If we drop a heavy tool or weight belt, the Plexiglas might shatter and fill the water with an exploding column of air.

As soon as our undersea workshop becomes functional, we'll use it for storing equipment, communicating with each other and as a refuge for a diver in trouble. We'll sit inside—relatively warm and without our diving apparatus—and study the ocean floor, the surrounding water and the ice overhead. Our transparent outpost on the Arctic continental shelf will be a window into the world's northernmost ocean.

Sub Igloo is not just a new technology. It's an old idea. It's the belief that you can only understand a new frontier by spending time inside it, exploring all its dimensions, trying to comprehend its multiplicities. Like *Sublimnos,* it confirms that some of this understanding can be gained with a good team of men and a modest amount of money.

Without warning, Nuytten and I look hard at each other and make a wordless decision. We have been in the water long enough. We nod and point up to the ice. It is time to return to the surface.

I lean away from *Sub Igloo* and press a round valve on the front of my inflatable suit. Air hisses softly against my chest, and the added buoyancy carries me up toward the ice.

Seen from below, the massive polar pack resembles a faded pearl ceiling. Our spent breathing air lies flat against it like thin pools of silver-blue mercury.

I am rising too fast, so I empty air from my suit by pressing an exhaust valve, but it is too late. With my legs and arms outstretched, I hit the ice with a balloon-like bump and set off a shimmering explosion of silver crystals. I let out a little air and kneel upside down on the flat underbelly of the ice.

To stand erect with my head downward requires me to use buoyancy to overcome gravity, but the first thing is to reorient myself visually. Slowly, the ice becomes a floor and the seabed becomes a ceiling, from which *Sub Igloo* hangs like a chandelier.

From my kneeling position, I attempt to stand. The legs of my suit fill with air and my 50-pound weight belt shifts down toward my head. I move slowly, because any quick action will tip me backward. Finally, I am standing—upside down. The ice stretches out below my feet and fades into a blurred horizon. To preserve my equilibrium, I move forward with awkward stiffness. Nuytten is right behind me.

Together, we shuffle forward and head toward the square-cut dive hole. The gleaming, white roof beneath our feet is six feet thick, strong enough to support the weight of a 747 jumbo jet.

The ice began to form about four months ago when the temperature suddenly dropped and a layer of frazel ice, thin and highway-smooth, formed on top of the sea. Soon after, the wind broke it up into countless small pieces that bumped together and rubbed against each other.

When the wind quieted, new ice formed between the broken pieces, locking them together into a rough, craggy surface. More ice froze onto their underside—quickly at first, and then more slowly as the ice became thicker. Within days, the liquid ocean became solid non-land.

The ice above us is part of a sprawling white roof that covers more than five million square miles. Its vast unsparing beauty touches the coastlines of Canada, the United States, Greenland, Norway and the Soviet Union. It's a beauty that leaves me greatly subdued.

When I was a schoolboy, I looked at the great white spot on the roof of North America and wondered what it would be like to go there. And now I am inside the world's least-known ocean looking at things I do not truly recognize and forces I do not really understand. The blood-chilling cold and weathered whiteness of the ice is beyond any language I know.

As I near the edge of the dive hole, I see two faces looking through the water and the warm yellow ceiling of the dive tent. The inviting opening seems to be below me, so I dive into it, headfirst.

Suddenly I am reoriented by the blaze of light and voices in the tent. Doug Elsey reaches down, wraps his fingers around my air tank and helps me up. When I take off my mask, a wave of warm air caresses my face. Someone strips off my gloves and pours warm water over my chalky white hands. A dull throb starts in both wrists. As I reach for a cup of hot coffee, I remember the words I first heard during *SeaLab 3*. "Pain is just another way of getting information."

Nuytten's head and shoulders appear in the ice hole. He drops his mouthpiece and pauses to catch his breath. He is breathing heavily, each exhalation showing as a gray puff above the water.

A fresh tank of air is slid into my harness and someone I can't see adjusts its straps. Another man is doing the same for Nuytten. For safety reasons, at least one person on the surface is responsible for each diver in the water. "Safety first, second and last" is something I learned from

George Bond. "Keep your team small and your technologies simple" is something I learned from Ed Link. "There is nothing like the burden of responsibility to promote accountability" is something I learned from both men.

Nuytten and I sit side by side at the edge of the dive hole, gaining back some of our lost heat. We take advantage of the break to check over the ongoing work with our teammates. Tim Turnbull, a doctoral candidate in marine biology, is waiting for us to put *Sub Igloo* together so he can continue to collect specimens of small marine animals. During his dive, he will continue his evaluation of our closed-circuit breathing system, an advanced model of the one we wore at *Tektite 2*. It's the first time it is being tested in polar waters.

Roger Smith, a marine geologist from Queen's University, will take more core samples of the soft sediments lying under the nearby kelp beds. Roger is studying the mineral composition and source of these sediments. In a few months, when he analyzes his samples, he will find that some of them contain chemicals similar to Agent Orange, the herbicide used by the American military to defoliate the jungle in Vietnam.

We are at the end of a year when the number of Americans killed in Vietnam is approaching 50,000 and Strategic Air Command bombers are dropping tons of bombs on Laos and Cambodia. And President Richard Nixon is making the decision to pull U.S. troops out of a war they have been losing for years.

Nuytten and I discuss the final assembly of *Sub Igloo*. "We'll just tighten a few more bolts, and the hemispheres should be secure," I say. "Then we'll fill her with air and slip inside."

Nuytten is not so confident. "We will—if the bonding at the equator between the plastic and the aluminum holds."

Nuytten is a brilliant, self-taught inventor who started off as a commercial diver in Vancouver and then became president of his own company, Can-Dive Services. But his real passion is designing under-water machines. Driven by a desire to make diving safer, he wants to build a pressure-protective suit that will shield divers from the weight of the ocean.

A geyser of bubbles breaks the water in the dive hole and a diver's head appears in its center. Rick Mason, who is filming underwater for the National Film Board of Canada, flips back his face mask. His breathing is fast and labored.

After a few breaths, he explains that his regulator froze in the closed position and forced him to make an emergency ascent. "Sorry for all the splashing and thrashing," he says. "I'll get another regulator and get back to work."

Mason's calmness is impressive. Like everyone else on the expedition, he quickly adapted to the hazards of Arctic diving, including the frequent mechanical failures and physical hardships. He's also comfortable with the psychological stresses: the darkness that swallows a diver in seconds, the floating fear of being trapped under the ice.

A fully-suited Doug Elsey joins Nuytten and me at the edge of the dive hole. After a few words about what we are going to do next, the three of us make the long glide down to *Sub Igloo*. We take up our position around the equator, tighten the last bolts and begin to fill the sphere with air. A stream of bubbles boils up into the interior and drives the displaced water out through the open bottom hatch. The structure trembles with tension, but there are no leaks.

When the air inside is below the equator, I exhale, pull myself down to the bottom of the sphere and slip up through the entrance hatch. When my head breaks the surface, I remove my mask and hear the echo of my breathing. Cautiously I look around.

The water level is just below my chin. Small cakes of ice float away on the wind of my steamy breath. The clear, curving walls of *Sub Igloo* seem not to exist.

I climb up on the circular bench and sit quietly. Outside, Nuytten and Elsey give me a thumbs up. Elsey points beneath the bench. I lean over to look and see two small fish. I am in the polar ocean's first under-sea fishbowl.

Sub Igloo is a prototype, so we are going to have to test it over long periods and in varied locations. But in its field trials in the Great Lakes and in its construction up here, we have learned that it can be easily

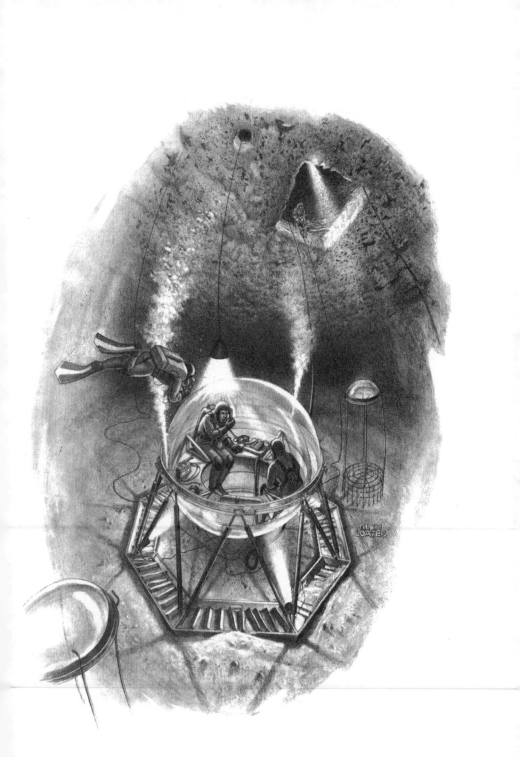

Sub Igloo, the world's first manned polar station, under the
five-foot-thick ice of Canada's Northwest Passage. *(Courtesy of Glen Loates)*

assembled underwater without the use of heavy equipment. We are hoping it is the forerunner of similar structures that will enable humans to live on the Arctic continental shelf.

⋄⋄⋄

The world's largest continental shelf is in the Russian Arctic. Driven by strategic interests, the Soviets have spent decades conducting major scientific programs on the ice in this region. A few years ago in the southern part of Russia, they began building small experimental undersea stations. However, so far, none has been used in the polar ocean.

In four months, the Canadian government will send me to the Soviet Union as part of a scientific exchange program. In Moscow, I will talk with Pavel Borovikov, chief designer of *Chernemor,* the most advanced Soviet undersea station. The 26-foot-long *Chernemor* holds a crew of up to five men. "We are currently using it in the cold waters of the Black Sea off the coast of Bulgaria," Borovikov will tell me, "to a maximum depth of 50 feet. During the past three years, test crews and scientific teams have spent 4,000 man-hours in *Chernemor*. We have big plans for its future."

During my days in Moscow and Leningrad, I will be asked what happened to the *SeaLab* project, and I will tell the curious Russian engineers and scientists what is public information in the West: when Berry Cannon died, *SeaLab* was canceled.

What very few people know is that the U.S. Navy converted its *SeaLab* knowledge into a top-secret project. It began in 1971, when a small group of saturation-trained divers traveled across the Pacific Ocean inside the nuclear submarine USS *Halibut* to the continental shelf off Russia's Kamchatka peninsula. When the giant sub came to rest on the seafloor, the divers moved through an air lock to a pressure chamber outside the hull, swam down through the darkness and located a slimy bundle of five-inch wires.

The wires belonged to a telephone cable that ran from the Soviet Union's missile submarine base at Petropavlovsk to the Pacific Fleet headquarters near Vladivostok. When the divers placed a listening device on the cable, they gained access to the inner vault of Soviet secrecy, including tactical plans for upcoming patrols, technical problems of Pacific Fleet submarines and test-flight results of sea-based ICBM missiles. It was the beginning of a clandestine diving program that expanded into the Barents Sea and the Russian Arctic. *SeaLab* saturation-diving techniques helped provide the first inside look at the strengths and weaknesses of the Soviet Navy.

⬦

A few minutes later in Resolute Bay, Phil, Doug and Rick enter the sphere and, after a brief tussle with a stubborn cork, we celebrate *Sub Igloo*'s construction with a champagne toast. Then we lean back and enjoy the view.

There are lights everywhere. A 200-watt lamp shines down on the station. Another is fixed to one of its struts. Two divers illuminating a *Sea Shell* with their wide-beam flashlights. A strobe light pulses under the silver frame of the dive hole. The lights are alive and bright, but they are temporary. In a few weeks, when we are gone, this place will return to blackness and the great, deep danger of night.

As I look at the dark water behind my three friends, I realize the ocean truly has defined my life and is as powerful a presence in my mid-thirties as it was in my youth. But their exhausted faces tell the real story. Arctic diving isn't really very glamorous. It's mostly dirty, gritty and uncomfortable work. It consists of ordinary people trying to match the unknown forces of the natural world with something powerful inside themselves.

TWENTY-ONE

JUNE 1973. I am inside a twin-engine aircraft flying over the south-ern edge of the Florida Everglades. The rain slamming against the windows is so heavy that both engines seem ready to stall. It is not just the lightning and turbulence that frighten me, but the fact that it is so dark I can't see anything out the window except slanting sheets of water. Then, without warning, the aircraft drops sharply and breaks through into thick bands of sunshine.

Between the shattered clouds, the sky is the color of a gas flame. Off to the left, a thin gray waterspout funnels its way down from its mother cloud to the surface of the gleaming sea. Farther out, low mangrove islands float on the water like a pod of green whales. Far beyond them is Key West, the island on the edge of the American dream. And somewhere off to the southeast, next to the Gulf Stream, is a research sub holding four men whose lives have been transformed by an accident.

This morning, the story of their entrapment on the seafloor and the U.S. Navy's desperate attempts to rescue them is front-page news. Yesterday the men were attempting to recover a scientific fish trap when they became entangled in the wreckage of the USS *Berry,* a Second World War destroyer scuttled last year. They are inside the *Johnson-Sea-Link,* Ed Link's newest sub, about 15 miles southeast of Key West at a depth of 350 feet.

The USS *Tringa,* dispatched from Key West, reached the site yester-day afternoon. Last night, Navy divers made two unsuccessful attempts to free the sub. This morning an elite team flown in from a naval base in San Diego made a third attempt, but they too were unsuccessful.

No one is certain about the condition of the men inside the sub. According to the *Miami Herald,* Jock Menzies and Bob Meek are in the pilot's sphere talking to *Sea Diver,* Ed Link's 100-foot-long research vessel, on their underwater telephone. There is no report on the status of Al Stover and Clay Link in the diving chamber behind them.

I look out the window at the mighty angle made by the ocean and sky. The four of them have been buried under the sea for more than 24 hours. At depths greater than 300 feet, the ocean's temperature falls dramatically, so they must be very cold.

I try to imagine what it must be like inside the sub. They are hunched over in their two small compartments in the wan light. Their faces are gray and they are silent except when there is something important to say. Their early optimism has left them; only a flicker of hope remains.

All their thoughts and actions are focused on one thing—survival. They know that their shipmates on the surface are doing everything they can to recover them. In shadows growing colder by the hour, their only warmth comes from their undying belief in this act of brotherhood.

⋯⋰⋯

"Follow me," the officer says, "if we hurry, we can catch the crew boat." I missed his name when he introduced himself, but he's a naval commander so I follow him along the corridor of the base administration building, past the impromptu pressroom and down the stairwell. He takes the steps two at a time. The sleeves of his freshly pressed shirt ripple over his arms.

The crew boat's diesel engine is running, and only one line holds it against the pier. I hesitate on the concrete edge and then jump across the open space onto the gray deck. Two arms reach up to steady me. The line is cast off, and we back out into the open harbor.

We steam through the harbor entrance and turn left into the pale, crumpled water of Key West's main ship channel. Ignoring the No Wake signs, the pilot pushes the throttle up to full bore, and we head south between a line of markers decorated with brown pelicans and cormorants.

Research vessel *Sea Diver* under way with the *Johnson-Sea-Link* sub on her stern. (*Courtesy of Glen Loates*)

From a sandbank near Crawfish Key, birds by the hundreds, including an osprey with a small fish still hanging from its talons, rise into the sky. At the outer buoy we make a slow turn and head toward Western Sambo Reef.

In the hour it takes to get to the deep blue waters off American Shoals, the men on the crew boat tell me what they know.

⋯⋄⋯

At the time of the accident, the seas were as calm as they are today and the Gulf Stream was running at about two knots.

The day before, the sub had placed a small fish trap near the stern of the USS *Berry*. The *Berry* is 390 feet long, 40 feet wide, and is lying on her port side.

A year ago, when the *Berry* was scuttled to create an artificial reef, seven 45-foot flagpoles were welded to her main deck. The flagpoles were used as reference markers to determine her location as she sank. Each pole was supported with eight 3/8-inch steel cables.

Yesterday morning at about nine o'clock, the sub made a dive to retrieve the fish trap. The visibility was poor. On the third attempt, the sub's stern swung toward the *Berry*. When the pilot tried to back up, he discovered he couldn't move more than 20 feet. The sub may have been caught in a cable of the aftermost flagpole.

The pilot reported his situation to *Sea Diver,* who called the coast guard for assistance. The coast guard asked the Navy to send out a search and salvage vessel.

The men in the sub considered making a lockout dive to free themselves, but decided it was too risky.

Yesterday afternoon, while waiting for the *Tringa, Sea Diver*'s crew lowered a weighted line to the bottom to guide the Navy divers directly to the sub. Strong currents kept the line away from the sub.

The water temperature at the sub's depths is about 48 degrees Fahrenheit. Inside the pilot's compartment, the four-inch acrylic sphere and heat from instruments is providing some insulation and warmth for

Meek and Menzies. The diver's chamber is made of aluminum and is not insulated. Its temperature has fallen to 48 degrees. Anticipating a short dive, Link and Stover are only wearing shorts and T-shirts.

At 48 degrees, the effectiveness of Baralyme to remove carbon dioxide is dramatically reduced. The carbon dioxide in the diving chamber is in the toxic range.

At 10 o'clock last night, two divers from *Tringa* made the first rescue attempt. Dressed in helmets and canvas suits, they were lowered on a stage to 316 feet and saw the sub below them. The ship's superstructure— masts, cables and a 25-foot radar reflector—blocked their access and they returned to the surface.

At the same time, Link and Stover reported that the carbon dioxide absorbing capacity of their Baralyme was exhausted. They began breathing compressed air from their emergency breathing system. Soon after, they switched to 13 percent oxygen-helium.

Early this morning, *Tringa*'s divers made a second attempt. Again they were unable to penetrate the *Berry*'s superstructure and cable array. According to Meek and Menzies, it was about this same time that Link and Stover began convulsing. Soon after, they became comatose.

This morning at six, a Navy diving bell was lowered from *Tringa* to 280 feet. A diver swam out of the bell and headed down toward the sub, but encountered strong currents, became fouled in his gas hose and was forced to return to the bell.

I am having difficulty processing all these details. For Ed Link and the men in his stranded sub, help from the Navy was only 15 miles away. In spite of this, a bright sunny morning led to a dark night of terror. And within the clinical description of the rescue attempts is an appalling reality no one has articulated: Al Stover and Clay Link are almost certainly dead.

"What's the latest word?" I ask.

"A few hours ago, a commercial salvage vessel, the *A.B. Wood,* arrived at the site. She's got a four-pronged grapnel attached to a remotely operated TV camera. She's going to try to hook a lift line into the sub."

A few minutes later, on the sun-flattened water south of American Shoals, I see the hazy outline of *Sea Diver* cradled between the *Tringa* and the *Wood*. The swells running beneath them are as smooth as varnish. As we slowly approach the ships in the afternoon heat, I feel dazed and disconnected, as if watching a television show with the color unbalanced.

"It looks like they've got her up," says the sailor standing next to me. I follow his gaze to the stern of the *Wood*. Lying in the water next to the ship's black hull is a shimmer of aluminum and acrylic. The *Johnson-Sea-Link* is on the surface.

"Our radioman says the *Wood* hooked her with its grapnel. The two men in the forward compartment are okay."

When the sub broke the surface, there must have been a hundred hammering hearts on *Sea Diver* and *Tringa*. Pulling the sub free from the rusted hulk of steel with its cross-weave of cables and platforms was a desperate gamble to save the two men in the pilot's sphere.

The commander comes up behind me and places his hand on my shoulder. "Mr. Link would like you to come on board as soon as you can."

The crew boat stays clear until Meek and Menzies are transferred to *Tringa*'s decompression chamber. Then we come alongside *Sea Diver* and I jump across to her main deck.

The men standing next to the hydraulic crane are running on nerves and no sleep. There is nothing for them to do but await the outcome. If their eyes turn to anything it is to check on each other. The only flicker of comfort comes from knowing that whatever is happening is happening to all of them.

Each man is struggling with questions that will haunt him for the remainder of his life. What if the chamber had been insulated? What if Al and Clay had more clothes and more Baralyme? What if the sub had a distress buoy?

I make my way down the familiar stairwell to Ed Link's cabin and knock gently on the door. It opens slowly. My old friend is barefoot and wearing dark shorts and a wrinkled shirt. His lips are sunburned. He is wiping his glasses with slow, circular motions of his thumb.

I don't know what to do so I step into the room, wrap my arms around him and give him a long hug. His body is trembling.

There are no words for this. In one prolonged instant, Ed Link lost two of his men, including his son. In his tear-stained face, I see anger, guilt and defeat. It is the defeat of a good man whose life is ruled by Victorian virtues and the old rules of the sea, the most important of which is that the captain takes full responsibility for whatever happens on his ship and to his men.

It is an unbearable loss, made worse by his role in it. Confident that it was only going to be a short dive, he allowed Clay and Al to step into the sub at the last minute—wearing the lightest of clothing. In spite of what he had learned from the loss of *Thresher,* he failed to equip his own sub with a distress buoy or adequate life-safety systems. To make matters worse, there was nothing in his thousands of hours of experience that could help him overcome the most important challenge of his life.

He looks down at the floor and keeps wiping his glasses. All the years of command have drained from him. Now, all he has left are his honesty and decency.

He asks me to go back to Key West, wait for the ship, and do what I can for the crew and their wives. Then, by his silence, he asks me to leave. The doorframe and the stairwell are made blurry by the tears in my eyes.

❖

Sea Diver is not due in port until tomorrow morning, so I take to the streets of Key West, wandering aimlessly past the white frame houses with their sprawling deciduous trees and sprays of scented flowers. I walk along dimly lit alleys past long, green vines hanging over broken fences. In places the sidewalks heave and slant, split by twisting, reptilian roots. Just after midnight, I slip into Captain Tony's and order a double rum straight up.

Usually when I am half drunk, there is a long, sweet spot when everything is possible—love, success, fame—but not tonight. Tonight there are only tumbling thoughts about four bodies hunched together in the growing cold and an old man, reeling from the events that have collapsed on him.

At this moment, I hate the goddamned ocean. I hate its size and its force. It is a malevolent son of a bitch whose currents and cold have just taken a good man's lifetime of effort and compressed it into tragedy.

A few more rums and I am back 10 years to the day I first landed in Key West. Since then I've had a family, a divorce and another family. I've made many mistakes, but, thanks to good luck and good people, I've built a career and spent thousands of hours inside the ocean. I've learned that that the two most important things in a sea-going life are your abilities and your choices.

Link was the first of those good people. He took a big gamble on an untested young doctor. He gave me advice, confidence and my initial fling at responsibility. Over the years, he became the kind of friend who is always there when you need him. Just last month, he encouraged me to take his small, inflatable undersea station on my next Arctic expedition.

It will take him years to get over this. He will recover and continue his pioneering work, but he will never be the same.

As the hours pass, I can't stop thinking of that small white ship anchored in the darkness on the edge of the Gulf Stream. Lying on his bunk, unable to sleep, is a man overcome by the despair that can overwhelm the bravest of men who find themselves on the wrong side of chance.

TWENTY-TWO

OCTOBER 2001. She is a big tarpon with unblinking eyes that make you feel like prey, and she is coming out of the blue, gliding through slanting pillars of sunlight. When she turns, her large scales gleam bright silver from gills to tail. Her belly shines like a mirror. She is the mystery of the Gulf Stream made manifest.

After she passes from view, I examine the ring of stainless steel bolts that secure the large view port into the side of the station. Because the air inside—the air that I am breathing—is 75 degrees Fahrenheit and 75 percent humidity, there are no signs of corrosion.

I turn away from the view port to study the interior of *Aquarius*. The table that holds my notebook has seats for four people. To my left is a comfortable six-person bunkroom lit by another luminous view port. In front of me is a small kitchen with shelves full of food, a sink with hot and cold water, a refrigerator and a microwave oven. Nearby are the station's life-support controls and a lab bench full of instruments. The only other person in the station is a technician hunched over one of the computer workstations. I am acutely aware of the two ceiling-mounted video cameras that record every move I make.

Almost four decades after I began working as a diving physician, I have been invited to visit "America's inner space station," a $10-million facility described by its staff as "the world's only laboratory that allows scientists to live and work under the sea." *Aquarius* is located at a depth of 60 feet next to a coral reef in the Florida Keys National Marine Sanctuary. Painted yellow and encrusted with thin layers of coral and algae, she is 43 feet long and 12 feet in diameter, and weighs 82 tons.

She squats on top of a 116-ton base plate designed to anchor her through the rising water and winds of killer hurricanes.

Three hours ago at the Mission Control Center in Key Largo, I spent an hour with Dr. Steve Miller, the marine scientist who directs the *Aquarius* program. He showed me the "watch desk" with its life-support system monitors, VHF radios, cellular telephone, sound-powered telephones and a quartet of video monitors—all connected by wireless telemetry to *Aquarius* 10 miles away. Steps from where we stood in the two-floor building are docks, boats, offices, laboratories, an electronics shop, equipment storage rooms and a decompression chamber.

"*Aquarius* has been operational since 1993," Miller told me, "and more than 200 scientists have participated in 50 ten-day missions. The station is the centerpiece of a research program focusing on Florida's fragile and economically important coral reefs."

Intense and soft-spoken, Miller is a botanist and expert in coral reef ecology. "Coral reefs are the marine analogue of terrestrial rainforests," he says, "home to more than 30 percent of the 160,000 known marine species. Unfortunately, they are among the world's most threatened ecosystems."

I asked him where the threats are coming from. "Coastal development, sewage pollution, overfishing, disease and climate change. Today, more than 10 percent of the world's corals are dead and dying." His voice trails off.

I gaze out the view port into a radiant blue ocean. We are 10 fathoms below the sunlit surface, perched on the western edge of the Gulf Stream, the antique sea road of container ships, oil tankers and long-ago treasure galleons. Inside its slow-motion currents, everything is changing shape and becoming something else.

It's hard to believe how quickly the years have gone by. In 1964, *Sea Diver* sailed within a mile of where I am sitting, heading north to a shipyard in Miami where a decompression chamber was added to the equipment on her main deck. On board was a young, freshly minted diving physician. I can see him now. He's wearing salt-stained dungarees with the lower legs rolled into bunchy cuffs and a navy-colored T-shirt with the words *Sea Diver* across its front. He's standing on the main deck talking to a man more than twice his age wearing thick glasses and looking like an English professor.

Most of the men I worked with in those early days are no longer alive. Ed Link passed away in 1981 and George Bond in 1985. In 1997, after a state funeral in Notre Dame Cathedral, Jacques Cousteau was buried in France. They were men who taught me to study the ocean for second meanings and deeper connections.

"I think it's almost time for you to suit up and head back to the surface." Mark Hulsbeck's statement breaks off my reverie. Mark is one of the two live-aboard station specialists who work for the University of North Carolina at Wilmington. The university operates *Aquarius* for the National Oceanic and Atmospheric Administration. Since my arrival, Mark has shown me through the interior of *Aquarius* and described the current seven-day mission.

This is the fourth day of Project NEEMO, or NASA Extreme Environment Mission Operations. Three shuttle astronauts and their mission commander are using *Aquarius* to simulate life on the International Space Station. It is the first NASA undersea experiment since *Tektite 2,* and its purpose is to improve the training of shuttle astronauts.

The television cameras inside *Aquarius* are linked to the Johnson Space Center in Houston, where investigators monitor the compartment, which is similar to those inside the International Space Station. In here, the astronauts are measuring light, noise and other factors that affect life in a closed environment. They are also sampling some of the new dehydrated foods being developed by NASA.

When the astronauts are outside, they follow communication protocols that mimic space walks. On this dive, they are on the reef with a marine scientist collecting water samples and measuring the health of different species of coral. It is training them to deal with unfamiliar sciences, a skill that is vital on the space station.

I have the good fortune to know two of the astronauts. Dave Williams is a Canadian physician who flew a 16-day mission on *Columbia* and is now the director of life sciences for NASA. Mike Gernhardt has flown missions on *Columbia* and *Atlantis*. A former commercial diver, he studied pressure physiology with Chris Lambertsen at the University of Pennsylvania.

I have come to visit these men because, in this new century, *Aquarius* is one of the few places where the pioneering work of Bond, Link and Cousteau still means something.

Because of these three men, and the others who followed in their footsteps, some 60 undersea stations with names such as *Hydrolab*, *Helgoland* and *Prinul* were eventually built and operated off the coasts of Russia, Germany, Bulgaria and a dozen other countries. Those "homes" within the ocean changed forever how we think about the world's biggest ecosystem. However, by the 1980s, high costs and the potential for accidents forced them out of favor.

As was predicted in the 1970s, two emerging technologies helped shoulder them aside. Today, undersea machines called "remotely operated vehicles" allow humans to stay on the surface, where they are not exposed to cold, wetness and pressure. Protective suits keep divers in the same atmosphere as on land. Both technologies permit useful work and minimize the risks of deep and prolonged diving.

However, if the men inside *Aquarius* have their way, an undersea station might help prepare future astronauts for the two-year round-trip to Mars is one possible scenario. The station would be placed at a significant depth and tap into the energy of a deep-sea volcano. Its interior would be kept at a pressure of one atmosphere, the same pressure as the diving compartments of the mini-subs that shuttle its crews back and forth to the surface.

This future deep-sea station would be a low-cost way of studying long-duration isolation in a high-risk environment. Phil Nuytten, who built the highly successful one-atmosphere Newtsuit, is designing a one-atmosphere structure he hopes to locate on the Pacific seafloor 200 miles west of British Columbia. It would hold up to 10 working scientists, who would swim out in articulated, armored suits, complete their work, and then return.

I stand in the blue water just below the entrance hatch and slip into my scuba gear. Down here, the ocean is the primary enclosure and framing device. It's both palisade and horizon.

Even now, so many years after I began my undersea journey, I am still moved by the allure and threat of the great waters. I am also moved by a fierce allegiance to the three men whose vision made living inside the ocean possible—Link, Bond and Cousteau—and the many others, including Stenuit, Barth, Lindbergh, Lambertsen and Mazzone, who helped them turn their vision into reality.

Dave Williams and Mike Gernhardt are aware of this legacy. "Their science, technology and imagination lit up a whole new world," says Williams. "They enhanced the connection between humans and our home planet," says Gernhardt.

I look into the rippled surface of the water. The recent history of the first sea dwellers will be hard to keep alive. There are no museums or memorial parks down here, only geography, shadows and impenetrable darkness.

Keeping my head low, I duck under a slim apron of steel and push off into the buoyant blue. Beneath my fins are black umbilical hoses and cables leading up to the life-support buoy. The large, cylindrical buoy and its transmission tower hold two 40-kilowatt generators, two air compressors, VHF radios and a microwave broadcasting system. This evening, images of the astronauts inside *Aquarius* will be relayed from the tower to Houston onto the internet and then to thousands of computer screens in every part of the country.

The exterior of the station bristles with a veneer of green algae and coral. In this light, the station seems more like an outgrowth of the reef than a center for scientific research.

A large school of yellow-tailed grunts and an enormous Nassau grouper are swimming in the lee of *Aquarius*. They face into the current with a steady, unforced motion, reminders that everything happening in this lower world, from the snowfall of plankton to the vast migrations of fish, was happening long before the human family evolved and will be happening long after this millennium is over.

I can't stay here too long. Nostalgia is hazardous. See her and leave. Talk to her and run. Stay too long and you diminish her heart-breaking beauty.

As I ascend through the water, the bleached seafloor slowly expands around me. For long seconds I can still see the station balanced on a thin ribbon of light. Then it fades into blue.

For the moment I am alone inside the ocean where, for a few short years, we lived our dreams of exploration. It was a time when we were free to fail and succeed. It was also a time when we had the liberty to be afraid. This kind of fear—primal, intelligent—is one of the greatest gifts of the ocean because it leads to humility. We were lucky. We loved the ocean and, in its own inscrutable way, the ocean loved us back.

EPILOGUE

AUGUST 2003. I am standing on the back deck of the *Ares* watching the ship's wake unfold under a starlit sky. It is a pale, spreading ribbon suspended between a dark ocean, the Pole Star and the Big Dipper. The churning water just behind the stern is shot with bioluminescence.

We are in the Atlantic Ocean halfway between North America and Africa, steaming south toward our next dive site. Two miles ahead are the lights of a second vessel, the *Akademik Keldysh*. Operated by the Russian Academy of Sciences, *Keldysh* is the world's biggest research ship. Within her city-block length are 130 people and 17 laboratories. Secured to her main deck are two $20-million mini-subs called *Mir One* and *Mir Two*. Each slightly larger than a cube van, one *Mir* can take three people to 20,000 feet and work at that depth for eight hours. A few years ago, one of them carried me down to the rusting decks of the *Titanic*.

Steps away from where I am standing are two smaller subs, *Deep Rover 1* and *Deep Rover 2*. Their main feature is a transparent Plexiglas sphere that gives the pilot and observer 320 degrees of visibility. Mounted on the bow of *Deep Rover 1* is a three-dimensional, high-definition camera and pressure housing worth a quarter of a million dollars.

For the past week, we have been using all four subs to explore and film a submerged chain of mountains that slices down the middle of the Atlantic from the Arctic to the Antarctic. Most of the mountain range is in deep water, but there are a few places where it rises close to the surface.

Four nights ago, as an observer in *Deep Rover 2,* I had a brief glimpse of one of those places. We descended more than 2,000 feet to the summit of the Atlantis Massif, a mountainous dome-shaped structure.

The first thing I saw was a steep slope of gray-white rocks. Seconds later, our pilot, Tym Catterson, slowed our descent until we were just hovering above a line of boulders. All around us, among the silky shadows, were the spires, mounds and pinnacles of a volcanic vent field called "Lost City." Some of the volcanoes were extinct; others were active. A shimmering mixture of hot vent fluid and cold seawater topped the thermally active pinnacles.

The only creature we saw was a large deepwater fish in the clear water below us. Then, after a few fleeting minutes on the bottom, our starboard thruster malfunctioned, we lost radio contact with the surface and had to abort the dive.

The brief descent has a special significance for me because it was made exactly 40 years after my trip to Washington for my first conversation with Ed Link. It was a reminder of how little I knew when I started and how lucky I have been ever since.

Since the day at the Washington Navy Yard, I have had the good fortune to watch Ed Link and dozens of other ocean pioneers completely transform our view of the world's biggest ecosystem. Their insights and observations have allowed us to become the first generation to grasp the true size and complexity of the ocean.

In the early 1960s, no one knew about seafloor spreading or even that there was a range of deep-sea mountains and volcanoes that ran—like the raised seam on a baseball—for 46,000 miles through the Atlantic and Pacific right around the planet. No one knew that the Mid-Ocean Ridge was dotted with tens of thousands of hot springs teeming with new forms of life living independently of sunlight.

While Ed Link, George Bond and Jacques Cousteau were showing us how to live under the sea, other innovators were mapping the ocean from ships and satellites and building multi-beam sonars, extreme-depth submarines and the global positioning system. Still others were confirming that the ocean contained uncounted numbers of abyssal hills, earthquake-induced avalanches, underwater "storms" and unknown species of animals. All these discoveries have given us new ways of seeing the ocean and new analogies with which to understand it.

I take a long, hard look at the western horizon, where the sea blurs into the sky. The breeze blowing down the deck of the ship smells of hot steel and dried salt.

One of the most important things we've learned during the past 40 years is that the human family is changing the ocean forever. We've always caught as many fish as possible and used the ocean as a garbage dump, but these old ways of doing business are coming back to haunt us. Today there are almost twice as many people living on this planet than there were in 1960. We are finding that our fish-catching technology is lethal to shallow and deepwater stocks and our garbage is durable and deadly. "The damage is so pervasive," says Paul Dayton, a marine ecologist at Scripps Institution of Oceanography, "that it may be impossible to know or reconstruct the ecosystem."

There is the added threat of climate change. The fossil fuels we burn at such a prodigious rate are melting the polar ice caps and causing a rise in sea level. One theory suggests that climate change may realign major ocean currents such as the Gulf Stream and send Europe spiraling into a deep freeze.

Forty years ago, my interest was the health and safety of working divers. Now my focus is on the health and safety of the great waters that surround them.

We have no alternative except to save the ocean. It will not be easy, but it must be done. One of my convictions is that it will be achieved by the right people telling the right story at the right time.

One individual taking up the challenge is the man leading this month-long expedition into the Atlantic. James Cameron is best known as the producer and director of *Titanic,* the most successful Hollywood film ever made. But he's also an ocean explorer.

Cameron's passion for ocean exploration began when he was a teenager growing up in Niagara Falls, Ontario. In the mid 1960s, he started reading everything he could about the pioneering work of Cousteau, Link and Bond. In his mind's eye he lived underwater in their stations and swam out into the sea with their aquanauts. They inspired him to become a certified scuba diver and learn as much as he could about undersea technology. Before he was 20, Cameron was thinking about how he might incorporate the latest advances in undersea technology into his films.

In 1988, he displayed this technology brilliantly in *The Abyss,* an action-adventure story about an offshore oil drilling crew recruited by the U.S. Navy to salvage a downed nuclear sub. Combining luminous underwater photography with astonishing special effects, *The Abyss* incorporated into its story an extreme-depth undersea station, transparent mini-subs and a diver breathing an oxygenated fluid.

But Cameron's ambitions went beyond making films about the ocean. A true explorer, he wanted to make films *under* the ocean. This explains why he started the production of *Titanic* by chartering the *Keldysh* and the *Mirs* and making 12 dives to the Mount Everest of shipwrecks. It's the reason he made his Discovery Channel documentary on the *Bismarck,* and why he and his team went back to the *Titanic* to make a three-dimensional, high-definition IMAX film called *Ghosts of the Abyss.*

Ghosts of the Abyss took audiences inside the wreck of the *Titanic* with a team of undersea explorers. Combining the creative elements of a feature film with the unscripted elements of a documentary, the giant screen images made the audience feel as though they were deep inside the ocean with the explorers, sharing their risks, sensing their fear, seeing the story unfold through their eyes.

Cameron is taking a similar approach to this summer's expedition. He has invited a team of 10 scientists and science educators to participate in dives at Lost City and other vent sites in the Atlantic and Pacific. These young men and women are experts in microbiology, geophysics, astrobiology and planetary science. Two are NASA scientists, including an astronaut evaluating the expedition as an analog for future space missions.

In a way, though, the real stars of Cameron's new film are the microorganisms that dwell on the vents and the larger animals, including crabs, mussels and tubeworms, that live alongside them. Fueled by chemical energy rather than solar energy, these strange-looking creatures raise questions about how life emerged on Earth. They also raise questions about the possibility of life on other planets. These are some of the

Deep Rover 1 with director James Cameron behind the 3-D,
high-definition camera. *(Courtesy of Glen Loates)*

mysteries Cameron is exploring in his film, which he is calling *Aliens of the Deep*.

I look down the deck at the full moon rising over the *Deep Rover* subs. What excites me about this expedition and the film that will come out of it is that it is about two of the things that matter most to me: exploration and life. After all this time, I have discovered that life in the ocean—life on the planet—is much more precious than I once thought.

Tonight, the *Deep Rover* pressure hulls are empty except for the air-conditioning hoses cooling their interiors. Tomorrow morning, four explorers will climb into them, close their hatches and descend into the depths.

The long-ago dives we made in our quest to live in the sea and tomorrow's sub dives all require the same kind of courage—the principled bravery of true exploration. They complete a collective cognitive circuit, making the ocean's interior a mirror in which we see something of ourselves, and our hope of understanding and protecting the earth.

Cameron would blush if you mentioned it, but he embodies the spirit of the undersea journey begun by Link, Bond and Cousteau. He has Bond's boldness. He has the *grand seigneur*'s great sense of wonder about the depths. He has Link's ability to design and build the technology needed to work deep. And he has the vision and commitment to create a new version of the ocean's long story.

When Cameron splices together his thoughts on the subject, you can see where he might be going.

"We are the only species that can think about creation," he told me a few days ago. "We can shape it, extinguish it—and save it. Surely a species that can fly to the moon and dive to the floor of the ocean can find a way to save the seven seas and the magnificent life they contain."

Whatever happens, I'm going to sign on for the voyage.

FURTHER READING

Barth, Bob. *Sea Dwellers: The Humor, Drama and Tragedy of the U.S. Navy SeaLab Programs*. Houston: Doyle Publishing, 2000.

Chaikin, Andrew. *A Man on the Moon: The Voyages of the Apollo Astronauts*. New York: Viking, 1994.

Cousteau, Jacques. *The Living Sea*. New York: Harper & Row, 1963.

———. *The Ocean World of Jacques Cousteau*. New York: World Publishing, 1973.

———. *The Silent World*. New York: Harper, 1953.

Craven, John P. *The Silent War: The Cold War Battle beneath the Sea*. New York: Simon & Schuster, 2001.

Earle, Sylvia A. *Sea Change: A Message of the Oceans*. New York: G.P. Putnam's Sons, 1995.

Earle, Sylvia A., and Al Giddings. *Exploring the Deep Frontier: The Adventure of Man in the Sea*. Washington, DC: National Geographic Society, 1980.

Kunzig, Robert. *Mapping the Deep*. New York: W.W. Norton & Company, 2000.

Link, Marion Clayton. *Windows in the Sea*. Washington, DC: Smithsonian Institution Press, 1973.

Moore, J. Robert, ed. *Oceanography: Readings from* Scientific American. San Francisco: W.H. Freeman, 1971.

Prager, Ellen J. *The Oceans*. New York: McGraw Hill, 2000.

Siiteri, Helen, ed. *Papa Topside: The SeaLab Chronicles of Capt. George F. Bond, USN*. Annapolis: Naval Institute Press, 1993.

Stenuit, Robert. *The Deepest Days*. New York: Coward-McCann, 1966.

ACKNOWLEDGMENTS

FIRST OF ALL to Debbie, the love of my life. And to my children who each in their own way, inspired these words.

A special thanks to Glen Loates, whose wonderful drawings illuminate these pages. And to Andy Pruna and Bates Littlehales for their splendid photographs.

To Marilyn Link, Bob Barth, Scott Carpenter, Robert Stenuit, Roger Cook, Denny Breese, Ian Koblick, Doug Elsey and all the others who were there when it happened and helped bring truth to the text.

To all the members of the *Man-In-Sea, SeaLab, Conshelf, Sublimnos Sub Igloo, Tektite, Aquarius* and *Earthship* teams who were and are my teachers.

To Cynthia Good, Nicole de Montbrun, David Davidar, Martin Gould, Sandra Tooze and the production team at Penguin Group (Canada).

To Ed Clark, Dianne Smith-Sanderson, Chris Armstrong, Gavin Thompson and everyone else at the TD Friends of the Environment Foundation who inspire me to protect our home planet.

INDEX

Page numbers in italics indicate illustrations.

abalone, 105–6
A.B. Wood (salvage vessel), 216, 217
Abyss, The (film), 229
Acadians, 140
Agent Orange, 207
air embolism, 138
air hunger, 67, 175
Akademik Keldysh (research ship), 226, 229
Alaska, 199
Aldrin, Buzz, 189, 192
algae, 64, 92, 196, 204, 224
Aliens of the Deep (film), 231
Aluminaut (submarine), 118
amberjack, 85, 88, 155
American Civil War, 16, 40, 41
American Revolution, 140
American Shoals, 215, 216
amphipods, 204
Anderson, Birger, 203
Anderson, Lester, 84–85, *86*
animal experimentation, 35–37, 83, 165
Antarctic, 226
Apollo Command Module, 119
Apollo Saturn, 156, 188–92
Apollo 11, 188, 191, 195, 196, 204
Appalachian Mountains, 13, 28, 29
aqualung, vi, 90, 95–96, 157, 185
aquanauts, 85, *86,* 87, 146, 148, 167, 169, 177, 228

Aquarius (inner space station), 220–24
Archerfish (submarine), 82
Arctic, 183, 199, 226
    environmental protection of, 199
    Russian, 210, 211
    sovereignty, 199, 202
    Sub Igloo expedition, 201–11
Arctic Circle, 201
Arctic Ocean, 39, 186, 193, 206
Arctic Waters Pollution Prevention Act, 199
Ares (ship), 226
Argentia (NF, naval base), 115, 125
Argus Island, 84
Aristotle, 163
Armstrong, Neil, 189, 190, 191, 192
Ascension, 6
aseptic bone necrosis, 98
astronauts, 10, 119, 127, 147, 162, 188, 195, 196, 222–23, 229
Atchafalaya River (LA), 140
Atlantic Ocean, 6, *32,* 60, 226, 229
Atlantis (space shuttle), 223
Atlantis Massif, 226–27
Australia, 154
avalanches, deep-sea, 227
aviation technology, 9–10

Bahamas, vi, *32,* 60–72, 84, 87, 90, 107, 116, 126, 199

Baralyme, 67, 216, 217
Barents Sea, 211
barracuda, 63, 88
Barth, Bob, 84–85, *86,* 147, 154, 167–68, 169, 170–71, 172–76, 177, 178, 224
Bat Cave (NC), 82
bathyscaphe, 8
Bay of Pigs, 147 (*See also* Cuban Missile Crisis)
Beat Generation, 155
Beckman Company (CA), 45
Belize, 193, 195
Bermuda, 80, 89
Berry, USS (destroyer), 212, 215, 216
Bert, Paul, 164
Bethesda Naval Hospital, 177
Big Lyle, 142–43
Binghamton (NY), 9, 20
Bismarck (film), 229
Blackburn, Richard, 147, 169, 170, 172, 174, 178
Black Sea, 210
blowout-preventor, 33
body temperature, low. *See* thermal stress
Bond, George, vi, 83–84, 32, 145–46
  background of, 82
  as captain, 153
  death of, 222
  invents saturation diving, 82–83
  legacy of, vi, 33, 223, 224, 227, 228–29
  love of literature, 151
  memoir, 83
  perception of by others, 87, 148
  personal characteristics of, 82, 148, 153
  physical appearance, 151, *152,* 153
  relationship with Cousteau, 92
  relationship with Ed Link, 87
  on safety, 206–7

underwater research initiatives. *See* Genesis; *SeaLab*
boomers (submarines). *See* submarines, ballistic missile
Borovikov, Pavel, 210
bounce dives, 141
Bounty, HMS, 18
Bradley, Mark, 168
Breese, Denny, 112, 114, 115, 118, 122, 123, 125, 126, 129, 133
British Columbia, 193, 223
Brittany, oil spill, 194
Bruce Peninsula (ON), 182
Buffalo (research facility), 97, 141
Bulgaria, 210, 223
bull shark, 154
Bunton, Bill, 147
Bushnell, David, 164

Cajuns, 140
California Gold Rush, 105
Calypso (research ship), 92, 93, 94–95
Cambodia, 207
Cameron, James, 228–29, *230,* 231
Campoli, Bernie, 80–81, 83–84
Canada, 88, 98, 180, 199
  national ocean policy, 199–200, 202
  –USSR, scientific exchange, 210
Canadian Coast Guard, 110
Can-Dive Services, 207
Cannon, Berry L., 147, 166, 167–79, 184, 210
Captain Tony's (Key West), 54–57, 59, 218–19
carbon dioxide, v, 72, 75, 76, 77, 216
  analyzer, 35, 36, 45, 67
  poisoning, 177, 178
  scrubber, 46, 48, 71, 98, 112, 114
  sensor, 114
Caribbean Sea, 39, 60–61, 72, 113, 193
Carpenter, Scott, 127, 147, 154, 204
Carson, Rachel, 96

Castro, Fidel, 77
Catterson, Tym, 227
CBS Evening News, 127
Chaffie, Roger, 119
Chase, Roger, 177
chemical industry, 69
Chernemor (undersea station), 210
Chicago, 180
Chicago Tribune, 167
ciliates, 183
cisco, 183
cities, sunken, 10
civilians, Navy view of, 57, 80, 145
civil rights movement, 29
Cleveland (OH), 180
climate change, 221, 228
closed-circuit breathing systems, 30,
    185, 197, 207
coastal development, ecological threat,
    221
cod, 115, 120
Cold War, 1, 2, 19, 29, 87, 115, 125
Collins, Mike, 189, 192
Columbia (space shuttle), 222, 223
combat swimmers, 30, 57
computers, 104–5, 224
Connecticut River, 118
Conshelf projects, 34, *91,* 96, 110
Conshelf Three, 90, 157–59
continental shelf, *32*
    Arctic, 202, 205, 210
    Bahamas, 60, 69, 73, 74, 127
    California, 162
    Canada, 199
    Caribbean, 39
    geology of, 31, 33
    Gulf of Mexico, 38–39
    North American, 2, 4, 11, *32,* 119
    Russian Arctic, 210
    world's, 17, 19, 31
Cook, Roger, 112, 113–15, 116–17,
    119, 120, 122–23, 124, 125

coral reefs, 26, 80, 88, 155, 195, 220,
    221, 224
Cornwall (England), 194
Cornwallis Island, 201–2
Côte d'Azur, 93
courage, viii, ix, 46, 47, 66, 74, 151,
    231
Cousteau, Jacques, vi, viii, 33, 83, 90,
    92, 110, 147, 163, 231
    appeal of, 92, 93, 95, 165
    death of, 222
    documentaries, 92–93
    experiments, 34, 164–65
    on food, 94
    legacy of, vi, 95–96, 223, 224, 227,
        228–29
    and media, 93
    personal style of, 93
    physical appearance of, *91*
    relationship with Link, 93–94
    on selecting divers, 95
    on undersea technology, 90, 92
Cousteau, Philippe (son of Jacques),
    90, 147, 148, 149–50, 155–57,
    162–63, 166
    on Cousteau name, 156
    participation in *Conshelf Three,*
        157–59
    on space program, 156
crabs, 229
Crawfish Key (Key West), 215
Creason, Robert, 177
Cronkite, Walter, 126–33, *134*
"crush depth," 4, 5
ctenophores, 204
Cuba, 39
Cuban Missile Crisis, 39 (*See also* Bay
    of Pigs)

Dayton, Paul, 228
decompression chamber. *See* submersible
    decompression chamber

decompression schedule, computerized,
104–5, 108
decompression sickness, 13, *14,* 15,
33, 138
Deep Diver (research submarine), 110,
111, 112–17, *121*
    Cronkites's lock-out dive, 127–33,
    134
Deepest Days, The (Stenuit), 74–77
Deep Rover 1 (mini-sub), 226, 229,
230, 231
Deep Rover 2 (mini-sub), 226–27, 229,
231
Deep Submergence Systems Review
    Group, 9, 12, 17, 19
    Thresher disaster report, 10–11
deep terrace reefs, 80
deepwater search, problems of, 7
De Lorena, 163
Detroit, 180
Dickson, Jim, 30, 31, 46, 71
Discovery Channel, 229
distress buoys, 17, 217, 218
diver mobility, 110, *111,* 112
divers–extreme-depth
    medical criteria, 95
    oil fields, 98, 103, 138, 140–44
    professionalism of, 163
    profile of, 100–5, 106–9
diving
    Arctic. *See Sub Igloo*
    clandestine, 210–11
    commercial, 33, 105
    mini-sub, complexity of, 117–19
diving helmets, *25,* 26, 100, 102, 105,
    106, 151, 153, 203
diving medicine/space medicine,
    compared, 187 (*See also* ocean/space
    exploration)
diving suit, *25, 26*
    armored, 223
    canvas, 100, 102
    cold-water, 203

hot-water, 171, 173–74
one atmosphere, 223
neoprene, 126, 162, 169, 171, 177,
    178, 180, 182, 204
pressure-protective, 184, 207, 223
rubber, 112
drill pipe, 33

Elk River, USS (ship), 161, 170
Elsey, Doug, 180–81, 182–84,
    185–87, 206, 208, 211
Emery, Alan, 182
England, 194–95
environmental protection legislation,
    199
equalization valve, 71–72, 75–76, 77
Experimental Diving Unit (DC), 16,
    30, 114, 145
extreme depth submarine, 227

face mask, 126, 132, 173
Falkland Islands, 6
fear, 17, 46, 47, 97, 99, 158, 225
Ferris, DC ("Direct Current"),
    137–41, 144
fire, malfunction, 114, 118–19
Florida Atlantic University, 155, 180
Florida Everglades, 212
Florida Keys, v, vi, 38, 81 (*See also* Key
    West)
Florida Keys National Marine
    Sanctuary, 220
food, dehydrated, 222
Fort Lauderdale (FL), 27
fossil fuels, 228
France, 92, 96
Franklin, Benjamin, 29–30
French Riviera, 33
frontier concept, 16, 28, 132

Galilee, Sea of, 10
gas analyzer, 45, 69, 75, 161
gas embolism, 130

gas exploration, underwater, 19, 98, 112, 194 (*See also* oil industry/offshore drilling)
Gellhorn, Martha, 54
Gemini (spacecraft), 10
General Precision, 94, 97, 164
Genesis Research project, 82, 85
Georgian Bay (ON), 182, 184–85
Germany, 223
Gernhardt, Mike, 222–23, 224
Ghosts of the Abyss (film), 229
Gilbert, Perry, 154, 155
Ginsberg, Allen, 155
glaciers, 31, 183
Glenn, John, 127
global positioning system, 227
Grand Bahama Island, 126
Grand Banks (NF), 119–20, 123
Greater Lameshur Bay (U.S. Virgin Islands), 195
Great Lakes, 24, 180, 208
Great Plains, 16
Great Stirrup Cay (Bahamas), 60, 69
great white shark, 154
Greenland, 206
Grissom, Gus, 119
grouper, 68, 73, 85, 88, 194, 224
Gulf of Mexico, 6, 33, 38–39, 60, 98, 112, 116, 136, 137, 138, 140, 142
Gulf of St. Lawrence, 6
Gulf Stream, 39, 60, 72, 78, 119–20, 155, 212, 215, 219, 220, 221, 228

Haight-Ashbury (San Francisco), 157
Haliburton wire, 137
Halibut, USS (nuclear sub), 210
Halley, Edmond, 163–64
Hall of Gems (National Museum of Natural History), 160
Halsbeck, Mark, 222
Hamilton, Bill, 102, 108
hammerhead shark, 155
hand-cranked submarine, 164

Harbor Branch Oceanographic Institute, viii, 165
Harvey, John "Wes," 1, 5
Hatteras, Cape (NC), 80
H-bomb(s)
    Cuban Missile Crisis, 39
    recovery of, vi, 116, 118
Helgoland (undersea station), 223
helium, 33, 36, 67, 68, 72, 73, 78, 100, 102, 103, 104, 164, 177 (*See also* oxygen/helium)
helmets. *See* diving helmets
Hemingway, Ernest, 39, 40, 54
herring, 115
Homo aquaticus, 96
hot springs, 227
hot-water suits, 171, 173–74
Hungry i (San Francisco), 155
Hunter's Point (San Francisco Bay), 146, 155
Huron, Lake, 180, 182, 184
hydrocarbon reservoirs, 33, 69
Hydrolab (undersea station), 223
hydrophones, 7, 88, 114
hypothermia, 33, 171, 172, 203

ICBM missiles, 211
Ice Age, 31
Igloo (inflatable workstation), 126, 133, *134*
Institute of Environmental Medicine (University of Pennsylvania), 20, 28, 30, 31
International Space Station, 222
internet, 224

Jeanne Marie (abalone-fishing boat), 106
jellyfish, 204
John Cabot (Coast Guard ship), 110, 113, *113*, 115, 117, 123–24
Johnson, Lyndon Baines, 129
Johnson-Sea-Link (submarine), *vii*, 165
    accident, 212–13, *214,* 215–19

Johnson, Seward, Sr., viii, 165
Johnson Space Center (Houston), 222, 224
Jones, John Paul, 16

Kamchatka peninsula (Russia), 210
Kelly, Pat, 104, 108
Kennedy, John F., viii, 28, 39, 129
Kennedy Space Center, 119
Kerouac, Jack, 155
Key Largo (FL), 221
Key West (FL), v, 17, 38–42, 48–49, 54–59, 212, 218
King, Martin Luther, viii, 29
Krushchev, Nikita, 39

Laos, 207
Labrador Current, 120
La Jolla (CA), 153
lakes, changes in, 184
Lambertson, Christian J., 20, 30, 31, 34, 223, 224
Lameshur Bay reef, 195
Le monde du silence (documentary), 92–93
Leningrad, 210
Life magazine, 81
Lil's Elbow Room (Morgan City, LA), 142–43
Lincoln Memorial, 29
Lindbergh, Charles, 9, 66
Lindbergh, Jon (son of Charles), 224
    deep dive, 65, 66–69, 70–71, 72–76, 78, 107, 110, 158
    lecture, 160, 163–64, 165
Linde Division, Union Carbide, 97
Lineaweaver, Paul, 168
Link, Clay (son of Edwin), 62–64, 156
    death of, v, viii, 213, 216, 217–18
Link, Edwin, vi, 28, 30, 34, 41, 48, 61, 81, 180, 212, 231
    builds *Sea Diver*, 10, 18
    as captain, 69, 79
    commercial success of, 94, 165
    death of, 222
    death of son, v, vii, 217–18, 219
    deep dive, 69–71
    early career of, 9
    on education, 20
    establishes oceanographic institute, 165
    father of simulation industry, 9–10
    first long-duration dive, 33–34
    founds Ocean Systems, vi, 97
    health of, 44
    injuries, 51–54
    invents saturation diving, 83
    invents submersible decompression chamber, 10, 20
    legacy of, v, vi, viii, ix, 9–10, 92, 110, 223, 224, 227, 228–29
    and media, 93, 127, 133
    perception of by others, viii, 45, 74, 87
    personal qualities of, viii, 17, 20, 87
    physical appearance of, 12, 16, *21*
    relationship with Cousteau, 93–94
    relationship with son, 62–63
    residences, 15, 20
    on safety, 207
    and *Thresher* disaster, 9, 10–11, 17
    underwater archaeological surveys, 10
    as visionary, 19, 20, 224
    writings of, 18–19
Link, Marilyn (sister of Edwin), 28, 165
Link, Marion (wife of Edwin), viii, 15, 19–20, 165
Link Foundation, 160, 163–66
Link Foundation Fellowship program, viii, 28, 45
Link trainer, 9–10, 12, 54
listening devices, seafloor. *See* sound surveillance systems
Littlehales, Bates, 54, 56, 197–98

Little Havana (Miami), 77
lockout submarine, 165
Long Island Sound, 118
Los Angeles Times, 167
"Lost City," 227, 229
Louisiana, 39, 136, 140–44
Luibel, F., 177
Lunar Excursion Module, 204

MacInnis, Allister, 23–24
mackerel, 115
Manhattan, USS (oil tanker), 199
Man-in-Sea program, 110
Manning, Tiger, 84–85, *86*
Marden, Luis, 18
Mark Eight breathing unit, 162
Mark Eight diving helmet, 151, 153
Mark Nine breathing unit, 162, 169,
    171, 173, 177, 178
Mark One breathing system, 196
Mars, 223
Marseille (France), 34, 96, 165
Mason, Rick, 208, 211
Mazzone, Walter, 83, 224
McCann chamber, 1, 7, 18
McGean, John, *14*
McGill University (Montreal), 23, 82,
    146
Mediterranean Sea, 6, 10, 33, 39, 93,
    157, 163
Meek, Bob, 213, 216, 217
"men fish," 96
Menzies, Jock, 213, 216, 217
Mercury (spacecraft), 10, 147
Mercury-Atlas rocket, 127
Mexico, 38, 39
Miami, 60, 72, 77–78, 81
Miami Herald, 213
Miami River, 77, 78
microorganisms, 229
Mid-Ocean Ridge, 227
Miller, Jim, 196

Miller, Steve, 221
Mine Defense Laboratory (US Navy),
    168
Mir One (mini-sub), 226
Mir Two (mini-sub), 226
missiles, 161, 211, 229
Mission Control Center (Key Largo),
    221
Mississippi Delta, 136
MIT (Massachusetts Institute of
    Technology), 8
Monaco, 93, 157
moon landing. *See* Apollo Saturn
Morgan, Bev, 92, 98–109
Morgan City (LA), 97, 98, 112, 136,
    137, 140, 142
Moscow, 210
mountains, deep-sea, 226–27
multi-beam sonars, 227

Nahant, USS, 60, 70
NASA, 19, 195, 222, 229
NASA Extreme Environment Mission
    Operations. *See* Project NEEMO
Nassau, 126
National Defence, Dept. of (Canada),
    202
National Film Board of Canada, 208
National Geographic, 12, 18, 54, 180,
    197
National Geographic Society, 10, 45,
    164, 181
National Museum of Natural History
    (Smithsonian), 160
National Oceanic and Atmospheric
    Administration, 222
National Wildlife Preserve (FL), 190
NATO, 88
Nautilus (fictional sub), 26
Naval Board of Inquiry, 177
Naval Medical Research Institute (New
    London), 33, 178

Naval Oceanographic Office (DC), 147
Naval Undersea Warfare Center, 147
Naval Weapons Facility (Dahlgren, VA), 177
neoprene. *See* diving suit, neoprene
Newfoundland, 115, 119
New London Naval Medical Research Laboratory (CN), 31, 82, 147
Newport Beach (CA), 105, 106
Newtsuit, 223 (*See also* diving suits)
Niagara Escarpment, 182
Niagara Falls, 182
nitrogen, 33, 36
nitrogen narcosis, 33, 35–36, 78, 98, 194
Nixon, Richard, 207
Noble, Art, 54, 55–56
North Atlantic, 6, 80, 110
North Beach (San Francisco), 155
northern lights, 202
north magnetic pole, 202
North Sea, vi, 33
Northwest Passage, 199, 201
Norway, 206
Notre Dame Cathedral (Paris), 222
Nova Scotia, 140
Nuytten, Phil, 201, 203, 204, 205, 206–7, 208, 211, 223

ocean
    changes in, 184
    complexity of, 227
    force for change, 96
    as intelligence instrument, 89, 210–11
    living inside, 154–55, 158–59, 163
    mapping, 227
    mystique of, 2, 16–17, 19, 20, 63–64, 68, 92, 189, 197, 224, 231
    polar, health of, 199

preservation of, 228, 231
    and Saturn Apollo mission, 190
Oceanographic Museum (Monaco), 93
ocean/space exploration
    similarities, 188
    Project NEEMO, 222–23
    Tektite 2 program, 195
    (*See also* diving medicine/space medicine, compared)
Ocean Systems Inc., vi, 98, 99, 112, 137
    formation of, 97
    H-bomb recovery, 116
    plow recovery, 112–25
octopus, 68–69
Office of Naval Oceanographic and Experimental Diving Unit (DC), 16
Office of Naval Research, 83
oil industry/offshore drilling, vi, 19, 31, 33, 98, 105, 140, 194, 199
oil spills. *See Torrey Canyon* oil spill
one-atmosphere diving suit. *See* Newtsuit
Ontario, Lake, 13, 24
overfishing, 184, 221, 228
oxygen analyzer, 35, 36, 45, 67
oxygen/helium, 10, 33, 34, 45, 67–68, 98, 101, 122, 157, 161, 164, 169, 170, 172–73, 216
oxygen sensor, 114, 119

Pacific Fleet, 209, 210
Pacific Ocean, 153–54, 162, 210, 223, 227, 229
Palomares (Spain), 116
Panama City (Florida), 83, 168
Papa Tospide (Bond), 83
patch reefs, 80
Pentagon, 128, 162
Perry, John, 110
Persian Gulf, 33
pesticides, 96

Peterson, Chuck, 131, 132
Peterson, Mendel, 10
petroleum industry. *See* oil
industry/offshore drilling
Petropavlovsk (USSR missile sub base),
210
phytoplankton, 183
pilots
airmail, 9
carrier, 57
commercial airline, 9
submarine, reflexes of, 118, 119
Pitcairn Island, 18
plankton, 115, 224 (*See also* phytoplankton)
plutonium, 8
polar ice caps, 228
Polaris missiles, 161
polar ocean
health of, 199
dive station. *See Sub Igloo*
pollution, 96, 184, 194–95, 199, 221,
228
Port Royal (Jamaica), 10
Portsmouth Naval Shipyard, 1, 8
Poseidon missiles, 161
Prinul (undersea station), 223
Project NEEMO, 222–23
Pruna, Andy, 147
Purple Onion (San Francisco), 155

Queen's University, 207

radioactivity, 8
Raymond, Larry, 177
recirculating breathing system, 56
Red Sea, 34
Reeves, John, 169, 170, 174
remotely operated vehicles, 223
Resolute Bay (Cornwallis Island),
201–2, 203, 204
Rickover, Hyman, 8

rim reefs, 80
robots. *See* remotely operated vehicles;
undersea robots
Royal Canadian Air Force, 23–24
Royal Canadian Mounted Police, 193,
195
Royal Ontario Museum, 182
Russell, Joe, 54
Russian Academy of Sciences, 226
Russian Arctic, 210, 211

St. David's Island, 80
St. John's Island (Caribbean), 196
San Clemente Island (CA), 106, 161,
162, 167, 173, 183
San Diego (CA), 161, 212
San Francisco, 155–56, 168
San Francisco Bay, 146, 148, 157
San Francisco Naval Shipyard, 146
San Pedro, treasure of, 81
Santa Barbara (CA), 97, 98, 105
Santa Barbara Channel, 98, 103
saturation dives, 82–84, 94, 99, 116,
141, 145, 147, 148, 162, 210, 211
Saturn V (launch vehicle), 119, 190
Schreiner, Heinz, 104, 108
scorpion fish, 154
Scripps Institution of Oceanography,
228
sculpin, 183
Sea Diver (research ship), v, *vii*, viii,
10, 17–20, 34, 41–47, 48, 49,
51–53, 60–65, 66, 93, 126,
221–22
deep dive (1964), 64–72, 87–88,
90, 145
and *Johnson-Sea-Link* accident, 213,
214, 215, 216–17
Sea Dwellers (Barth), 85, 170, 171,
172, 173–76
seafloor colonies, 145, 158 (*See also*
SeaLab 3)

seafloor listening devices, 88–89
SeaLab I, 80, 81, 82–85, *86*, 87–88, 89, 110, 146, 147, 148, 178, 210–11
SeaLab 2, 147, 149, 153–55, 168, 178
SeaLab 3, 145, 146–51, 160–62, 181, 204, 206, 210
  death of Berry Cannon, 167–79
sea level, rise in 228
SEALs (US Navy), 112
Sea Shell (communications booth), 203, 204, 211
Second World War, 9, 23, 41, 88, 127, 212
Selwyn, Steve, 181
Sha'ab Rumi Reef (Red Sea), 34
sharks, 154–55
shipwrecks, v, 18, 81, 120, 182 (*See also* names of ships; Spanish treasure ships; treasure hunting)
shrimp fishing, 40
Silent Spring (Carson), 96
Silent World, The (Cousteau), 92
simulation industry, 9–10
Singer Corporation, 94, 97, 164
Skylark (sub rescue vessel), 1, 2, 4, 5, 6–7
Sloppy Joe's (Key West). *See* Captain Tony's
Smith, Roger, 207
Smithsonian Institution, 10, 160, 164
smoke inhalation, 114, 119
Somerset Island (naval station), 80, 81
SOSUS (sound surveillance systems), 88–89, 115
South Africa, 154
South Atlantic, 6
Soviet Navy, 1, 2, 88, 210, 211
Soviet undersea stations, 210
Spain, vi, 116, 118
Spanish treasure ships, 10, 61, 81, 221
Starfish House, 34
Star I (minisub), 85

Stenuit, Robert, 33–34, 43, 44, 45–47, 50, 56, 64
  deep dive, 64, *65*, 66–69, 70, 71–74, 78, 107, 110, 158
  legacy of, 224
  writings of, 74–77
Stephan, Admiral, 94
stingray, 64
Stover, Al, viii, 213, 216, 218
Strategic Air Command (US), 39, 207
Sub Igloo (undersea station), 186, 187, 201–10, *209*, 211
Sublimnos (undersea station), 180–86, 205
submarines
  ballistic missile, 2, 88
  early history of, 163–64
  extreme depth, 227
  hand-cranked, 164
  lockout, 165
  midget, 30
  nuclear powered, 1–2, 88–89, 112, 165
  pilots, 118, 119
  psychology of, 118
submersible decompression chamber (SOC), 10, 20, 33–34, 35–37, 48, 60, 64, *65*, 66, 71, 72, 73, 75
Summer of Love (San Francisco), 156–57
sunken cities, 10

Taylor, Vince, 112, 114, 115, 122, 124, 125
Tektite 2 (undersea station), 195–97, *198*, 199–200, 222
Texas, 39
thermal stress, 171, 172, 173–74, 177
Thompson, Robert, 84–85, *86*
Thresher, USS (attack sub), 1, 2, *3*, 4, 35, 116, 218
  casualties, 9

loss of, 5–7, 17
report, 10–11
search for, 7–9, 118
tiger shark, 154
Titanic (film), 228, 229 (*See also*
   Titanic, RMS)
Titanic, RMS, 120, 226 (*See also*
   Titanic [film])
Toronto (ON), 180, 181, 184
Toronto General Hospital, 13
Toronto Telegram, 188
torpedoes, 112
Torrey Canyon oil spill, 194–95, 199
Travis, Bob, 24
treasure hunting, 10, 26, 61, 81, 221
   (*See also* shipwrecks; Spanish treas-
   ure ships)
Trieste (bathyscaphe), 8, 118
Tringa, USS, 212, 215, 216, 217
Trudeau, Pierre, 193–94, 195–97,
   199–200
Tucker, Teddy, 81
Tuckfield, Cyril, 82
Turnbull, Tim, 207
21st Century, The (TV series), 127,
   133, 135
Twenty Thousand Leagues under the Sea
   (Verne), 24, *25,* 26, 83

Undersea Hunter (ship), 60
Undersea Medical Society, 145
undersea robots, 184 (*See also* remotely
   operated vehicles)
Underwater Demolition Team, 30, 57
"Underwater Man—His Evolution and
   Explorations" (speech), 163–65
underwater storms, 227
underwater telephone system. *See* UQC
Union Carbide, 94, 97, 164
United States Naval Academy, 1

University of North Carolina
   (Wilmington), 222
University of Pennsylvania, 20, 28,
   29–30, 67, 71, 223
University of Toronto, 13, 145
UQC (underwater telephone system),
   2
uranium, 8
U.S. Navy Sixth Fleet, 10, 116
U.S./Soviet relations, 88–89, 110, 114
   (*See also* Cold War; Cuban Missile
   Crisis; *SeaLab*)
U.S. Virgin Islands, 195
Utina, USS (salvage ship), 110, 115,
   117, 123

Verne, Jules, 24, *25,* 83
Vietnam War, viii, 42, 57, 59, 87, 98,
   127–28, 130, 157, 162, 207
Vladivostok (Pacific Fleet HQ), 210
volcanic vent fields, 226, 229

Washington Navy Yard, 12, 16, 227
Washington Post, 167
Wells, Paul A., 178
Western Sambo Reef (Key West), 215
wetlands, Florida, 190
wet suits. *See* diving suits
White, Ed, 119
Williams, David, 222–23, 224
Wilson Cove (San Clemente Island),
   161
Woods Hole Oceanographic Institute,
   7
Workman, Robert, 83, 178

yellow-tailed grunts, 224
YFBN–12 (Navy barge), 84
Yucatan peninsula, 39